Understanding Animals

Gerhard Gronefeld

Translated by GWYNNE VEVERS, M A, D Phil
and WINWOOD READE

Understanding Animals

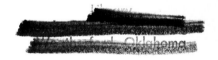

 THE VIKING PRESS: New York

Verstehen wir die Tiere?
© Georg Westermann Verlag, Braunschweig, 1963

Understanding Animals
Translation © William Heinemann Ltd., 1965

Published in 1965 by The Viking Press, Inc.
625 Madison Avenue, New York, N.Y. 10022

Library of Congress catalog card number: 65-19275
Printed in The Federal Republic of Germany

Contents

		Page
1	The Story of the Carrier-bag	9
2	A Different Bed Every Night	15
3	The Ape-man and the Anthropoid Apes	37
4	Mr Walther — the Buck Gazelle	43
5	The Quadruped	49
6	The Fight of the Stallions	78
7	Maxi — the Condemned Squab	83
8	A Dove with Two Dads	105
9	Under an Elephant's Foot	112
10	Elephant Dossiers	118
11	Elephants after Dark	141
12	Augusta's Take-over Bid	145
13	When Elephants Tremble	151
14	"This Is the Police Speaking . . ."	167
15	The Language of Ears and Trunks	171
16	The Confused Elephant	174
17	The Reform of an Irresponsible Father	176
18	Beautiful but Useless	180
19	Hermann Takes Pride of Place	195
20	The Young Monkey Who Was Afraid of Monkeys	210
21	Lord of the Island	215
22	When a Chimpanzee "Weeps"	219
23	How Not to Become Leading Ape	223
24	There Are Limits to Freedom	245
25	A Pyramid of Personalities	253
26	The Appeal of a Nursery	258
27	Wild Beasts	273
28	The Uncanny Cock	280
29	They Talk to Eggs	285
30	Learn or Perish	310
31	The Cock Who Thought He Was a Pug	315
32	One of Nature's Mysteries	317
33	Four Dachshunds Are Born	318
	Acknowledgements	320

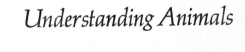

Understanding Animals

CHAPTER 1

The Story of the Carrier-bag

THE COURSE OF most of my studies of animals has been determined by chance observations. One Saturday morning in a small pet shop people were pushing their way up and down the narrow gangway between cages and aquaria of all shapes and sizes. Human voices mingled with the screeches of parakeets, the chatter of monkeys and the song of canaries.

"Six pennyworth of water fleas," piped a small boy, holding his jar up over the counter.

"Mind your backs, can I get through?" said a broad=shouldered man as he thrust his way to the front, swinging a large carrier=bag over the heads of the waiting customers. "Hey, Karl," he shouted to the shopkeeper, "someone left a young puppy with us, can you take it over?"

Karl Eiber, the pet=dealer, had already got more than enough to do but he looked up momentarily and recognized the burly man from the slaughterhouse. "Put it down at the back, I haven't time to deal with it now," he said. The man from the slaughterhouse shouted his thanks and the carrier=bag vanished under a tall monkey cage. The customers pressed forward, time passed, and in the bustle of week=end business the puppy was forgotten.

Later, there came a boy's shrill voice: "Do look, isn't it lovely!" Eiber glanced up briefly — everything in his shop was lovely to youngsters — but then he looked again, and could scarcely believe his eyes. Barbi, a female rhesus monkey tethered by a long chain, was sitting on the roof of her cage and with great concentration she was grooming a small black=and=white fox=terrier. The puppy! ... Two quick steps and Eiber reached Barbi: "That's not for you," he said and went to take the puppy from her. But Barbi was not prepared to let him take away her "child" and bared her teeth, screaming at Eiber; as he tried to seize the puppy, she bit him and drew blood. The puppy sat quite unmoved by it all; he had enjoyed being tickled and groomed.

A few days later I entered Eiber's pet shop and read the notice on the door: "Good home wanted for fox=terrier puppy — four weeks old." I remarked to Eiber: "So you also deal in dogs!" and that was how I came to hear the story of the rhesus monkey and the puppy.

I wondered if it would be possible to re=enact the sequence of events so that I could take photographs and make an attractive animal story in pictures. Would the monkey behave in a similar fashion? Eiber was not sure, but as he still had the puppy he was quite prepared to let me try and we fixed a date for the following Sunday, when the shop would be closed to the public.

The puppy was put back into the carrier=bag ready for the re=enactment. The female monkey had been well fed and was sitting as usual at the end of her long chain on the roof of her cage, where she was busy eating peanuts. She was quite used to strangers and accepted the opening and shutting of the shop door as part of the daily routine. When I entered the shop, holding the carrier=bag, she paid no attention. I exchanged a few words with the assistant behind the counter, just as the man from the slaughterhouse had done a few days earlier, and I placed the bag at the foot of the monkey's cage. Barbi was so busy cracking nuts that she had no time to show any curiosity; I was afraid that she had not noticed the carrier=bag. I took the opportunity to get my camera in position and then, as far as I was concerned, I was ready for action. But Barbi was in no hurry: she continued to eat, cracked another nut and ate yet another. It was surprising that the puppy remained still so long, but suddenly there was a whimper — the terrier was too hot. At once Barbi raised her head; she listened for a moment. Yes, there was the noise again. She gazed down at the carrier=bag and then in a flash she was alongside it. I was worried lest she should take the puppy out down on the floor, but she sniffed the bag from all angles and then, gripping the handle, she climbed quickly, hand over hand, still holding the heavy object, up to the roof of her home. She placed the bag in front of her and then opened it with such dexterity that it appeared to be a matter of routine. She had, of course, done it once previously. First she peeped inside, then plunged her head right down into the bag and at once withdrew it; her mouth opened with astonishment as she chattered: "he=he=he=he=he!" It was as though she were telling me that it really was a puppy in the bag. Then she pushed both hands into the bag and seized the puppy. With shrieks of delight she pulled the little chap out and put him down on the roof. The black=and=white terrier was remarkably sweet=tempered. The monkey laid him on his back and he allowed her to do just as she pleased. He lay quite still while she nibbled his claws and then cleaned his pads. Barbi worked as though she were trying to make up for lost time. All four feet were given a course of treatment, and when she was satisfied that there were no more granules between his toes, she turned him right side up. He gave no sign of resistance at any stage and Barbi was so preoccupied that she was quite oblivious of me. This was excellent from my point of view because I could take close=ups from all angles without disturbing them. Barbi gripped the puppy between her legs, holding him firmly with the toes of her feet, leaving both her hands free to groom his coat. While this was going on he lay as still as a mouse. Now and again he flicked his tongue over his moist nose. Barbi groomed him as though he were her own child.

Monkeys frequently groom each other but this was not an example of social grooming. The dog could not respond but it provided the necessary stimulus to the innate grooming urge of the female rhesus monkey. Strictly speaking, of course,

Barbi did not de=louse the puppy: she subjected him to a thorough course of body and skin hygiene as is the custom for monkeys — and not only monkeys. She bent back every little hair so as to get at the pores. She was looking for the scales which are frequently found there. A monkey likes the salty taste of scales and scale= hunting frees the partner from the continual need to scratch. This is why mon= keys "de=louse" and allow themselves to be "de=loused". So Barbi was behaving in the normal way for a monkey, but in addition she was behaving maternally: she possessed a natural urge to groom and this was stimulated by the presence of a youngster in front of her which needed mothering. The puppy had no objection to the tickling and was conscious of the warmth of another living creature which was keeping him company. He was about six weeks old and lacked a mother. With little chance of being scratched and kept warm by human beings, it was therefore not surprising that two such dissimilar species should huddle together and derive mutual satisfaction from their association. This charming picture had a sensible basis. I took the last photograph of Barbi grooming the little fox=terrier and was conscious of feeling I had finished the job satisfactorily. As I left Eiber's pet=shop, little did I realize that this was to be only the beginning of a full scale experiment.

The series of photographs lay in front of me, and as I studied them I was struck by the extraordinarily human facial expression and movements of the monkey. Barbi's delighted astonishment, the excited chatter as she made her dis= covery, the unpacking of the carrier=bag, the devoted motions of grooming — all this seemed very familiar to me, surely I had seen it somewhere before? Then I remembered. It was when my daughter Ingrid was still a little girl and she was playing with her dolls, brushing their hair, washing them and tidying their clothes — in effect grooming them — or when she was unpacking a new parcel. Then it suddenly dawned on me: some psychologists call a certain stage in human development "the chimpanzee stage". I made up my mind to find a child of the right age and study it again.

I spoke to Dr Lückert, who was then assistant to the Munich psychologist Pro= fessor Lersch, and showed him my pictures of the carrier=bag story. "That is indeed the 'Aha=stage'," exclaimed the psychologist, as he looked at the photograph of the female monkey showing astonishment.

In man the "chimpanzee stage" lies between the first and second years of life. It is so called because at this stage of mental development many parallels exist with that of the anthropoid apes. The apes, however, are not able to develop much beyond this stage. This I learnt from Lückert as we talked; I could not help wondering what would happen if a child in the "chimpanzee stage" were presented with a situation similar to the one to which the female monkey was accidentally exposed. It was during my conversation with the psychologist from Munich Univer= sity that I thought of conducting an experiment.

The fox=terrier had in the meantime acquired a master and was not available — but two days later I came across a four=weeks=old alsatian puppy and also three young children: Frederica, Ralph and Christian. Frederica, a charming little girl one and a half years old, became my first experimental human animal and I wondered how she would react.

The carrier=bag containing the puppy was placed in the room. Frederica was allowed in and the only help I gave her during the experiment was at the start. "Look, Fritzi," I said, "I wonder what's in that bag." Fritzi displayed no sign of shyness. The carrier=bag was fastened but she opened it with neat little fingers. The bag was large, its contents small. She peered into the darkness at the bottom of the bag and then exclaimed: "Ah=wow=wow," as she recognized a dog. At once she showed her astonishment. Her mouth became completely round. My psychologist friends would have been jubilant, had they been there: the "Aha=stage" in classical com= pleteness. Fritzi's behaviour spoke volumes. She made a face so like the monkey's that it was as though she had copied it. The same experience — the same behaviour pattern in man and in monkeys. Next Frederica dipped into the bottom of the bag and pulled the puppy out into the daylight, holding him by his tail, which is the best way with a woolly ball. She was delighted with the little alsatian: "Ei=ei," she said and pushed her face down on his rough head. This position was very uncomfortable. She sat down abruptly, pulled the puppy on to her lap and stroked his coat repeatedly. The little girl was no different from the female monkey: young as she was, she already possessed an active urge to look after the puppy. There was a direct parallel between the human child and Eiber's female monkey. But the reactions of the two boys were completely different and highly individual.

Ralph, who was a year and eight months old, went straight to the dog bag, just as Fritzi had done. He showed "astonishment" in the sense of my experiment, then pulled the puppy out. After this action, however, his curiosity diminished. He did not stroke him. On the contrary: he was unhappy when the puppy began to sniff him and started to cry and hit out at him. Then suddenly Ralph abandoned the puppy and directed his attention to the carrier=bag. He appeared to be working out if there could be anything else in such a large bag. He started to investigate — and was disappointed. Unlike the little girl, Ralph did not appear to have any grooming instinct or urge to look after the puppy; with him the urge to investigate was predominant.

Christian was the eldest of the three children; he was two years old and was already a definite little personality. He looked straight into the bag — and registered astonishment. So far the parallels were maintained. "Bow=wow," he shouted at the top of his voice as he saw the dog — and ran away. He showed no signs at all of taking the dog out but ran out of the room. He could not get to his playroom fast enough and his mother wondered what he could possibly want. When he came back he was beaming all over his face, and in one hand he held out his white woolly toy dog so that we could all see it. "Bow=wow=wow," he shouted and stuffed it instantly into the carrier=bag. It seemed natural to him to put the two dogs together. I am not sure if one could go so far as to say that this action represented an ability to categorize but one thing was quite certain: he showed no urge to groom or tend the puppy.

Of the four candidates in my experiment, the two males took a different course from the two females. The males' actions were based more on thought than on feeling: they were not tied to the object, they thought beyond it and both took individual routes; Ralph investigated and Christian put things in order. The two females, on the other hand, both reacted according to their natural feelings: their actions were determined by the emotional drive to care for and to tend. I won= dered if these results were evidence of the practical sense of the male sex and the emotional feeling of the typical female, with its deep sense of the need to preserve the species. The results appeared to me to be examples of instinctive behaviour.

Now I lacked only a male ape or monkey in order to complete my experiment. I decided that a male chimpanzee would be just right and so I went to the Ape Centre of the Munich Zoo at Hellabrunn and explained why I wanted a male chim= panzee. They were surprised by my request and I was told that my idea was not a good one. "If you put the carrier=bag in front of a male chimpanzee," they said, "we cannot guarantee what will happen and certainly not the safety of the puppy. A male chimpanzee is much too unreliable. They are very clever, much more so than people would ever think, and it is impossible to forecast what would happen. For example, the chimp might haul the puppy up and then drop it, either on purpose or by accident; he might dismember the puppy to satisfy the urge to investigate, or he might even kill it in a sudden fit of jealousy." They suggested that I should use a stuffed toy dog but I was unwilling to alter the form of the experiment. It was not safe, however, to ignore the advice of the Hellabrunn Zoo ape experts: it was quite clear that the reactions of a male chimpanzee under the conditions of my experiment would be totally unpredictable. The boys had also behaved in an unpredictable manner and for the sake of the puppy I dared not take the risk.

Finally the experts suggested that I should use a five=years=old female chimpanzee named Jenny. As she was more closely related to man than to a rhesus monkey, she seemed a fitting subject for rounding off my experiment. As it happened, she completed my observations in a way that I had not anticipated.

Jenny's sequence of actions was not only the same as that performed by the other two female experimental subjects; her movements were, in fact, identical with those of the little girl Frederica. The way in which Jenny dived into the carrier=bag, pulled the puppy out by the tail, and the loving way in which she touched his head were all similar. In fact the use of the limbs and the whole position of her body were so completely similar that one might have thought the little girl and the chim= panzee were imitating each other's performance. The final action of the chimpanzee displayed the same maternal aspect as that of Barbi. The "child" was taken up and tended — it was "de=loused" by the monkey and the chimpanzee and it was stroked and cared for by the human child.

The well=known student of animal behaviour Professor Heini Hediger, Director of the Zoo at Zurich, is trying to investigate by scientific method the behaviour patterns which have their origin in the relationship between man and animals. From his extensive observations he believes that under special conditions man and certain animals can meet on the same plane, at least momentarily, and as a result of this a direct understanding is possible. When Professor Hediger saw my photographs of Jenny and the alsatian puppy, he wrote: "The so=called 'de=lousing' is by way of being one of the chief occupations of apes and monkeys, and as a rule it is still misunderstood in zoos. In fact it has nothing to do with catching lice but is a ritualised skin grooming which has developed into a social ceremony. Apes and monkeys groom their companions in the Zoo, and may extend this to other species, even to humans, with whom they are on good terms. But they also expect to be 'de=loused' in return. Members of the same species naturally understand the rele=vant invitation, but it makes it much more difficult when they turn, for instance, to a puppy."

But in my experiment the difficulty never arose because after Jenny had "de=loused" the puppy I removed him immediately. The chimpanzee did not like it when I approached her and she looked as though she were going to rebel. With the help of a couple of bananas I was able to remove her "child" without difficulty. It is always on my conscience when I have tricked an animal successfully and I try not to let the victory over the animal appear too obvious. And this is what I now did with Jenny. I remained sitting near the chimpanzee, with the puppy in my arms, stroking him just as she had done. There was a wonderful sense of harmony between the three of us. Jenny squatted on the torn carrier=bag facing the puppy and carefully peeled a banana. And then something happened which could only have arisen in the peaceful atmosphere of quiet understanding that was established between the three of us: Jenny showed me something else that comes naturally to apes. She began to tear up the carrier=bag. I knew, of course, that apes are very destructive and that they are great wasters of food, but a few seconds later, she showed me what she was up to with the carrier=bag. Suddenly she stood up, came over to me and with her large mouth she "addressed" me and then, very carefully, she took hold of the puppy. I wondered whether to let her have him again; there was a definite risk that she would want to take him away with her back to the top of her cage.

A keeper was present during the whole of the experiment, ready to use his authority as "leading ape" in the event of Jenny's having a sudden fit of rage. I warned him to watch out and then, feeling decidedly anxious, I let Jenny have the puppy. Fortunately my fears were completely groundless. Very carefully the chimp took the puppy in her hands and put him down in the middle of the paper. She then picked up other scraps of paper and laid them on top of and around the puppy. It was slightly alarming for the puppy, which tried to wriggle away from the rustling material. Jenny restrained him gently but firmly and put her mouth against his nose and rubbed it soothingly. Then she took the remains of the bag, sat down on it and wrapped it all round herself and the puppy. You may well ask what all this was for. It was Jenny building a nest for herself and her "child", just as chim=panzees do in the wild.

CHAPTER 2

A Different Bed Every Night

STRANGE AS IT may sound, anthropoid apes not only build nests but they do it more than once a day: one for the midday siesta and another, in a different place, for the night. Gorillas do this and so do the orang=utans of Asia. Every night they sleep in a different bed, at widely varying heights in trees. The nest for the midday siesta, as a rule, is built not far above the ground.

Nests built by anthropoid apes can scarcely be described as works of art. The apes mostly drag convenient branches into a heap and interweave them very roughly, adding more branches and leaves on top. Gorillas build their nests on the ground or occasionally at low heights from the ground. This is because of their enormous weight; one of these apes, for instance, may weigh up to six hundred=weight.

I found the sleeping nests of the mountain gorilla in the border country between Uganda and the Congo, at a height of about 9,000 feet on the slopes of the Muha=vura Volcano. These were clumsy structures, suitable only for one night's rest, and in no way resembled the artistic nests of birds.

The orang=utan, which lives in Borneo and Sumatra, is the best nest=builder among the anthropoid apes. They venture right up in the trees, where they weave a firm platform which is sufficiently solid to support their considerable weight — even though this may well be as much as a hundredweight and a half. In zoos one can observe time and again how the anthropoid apes like to draw sacks or some kind of covering over their heads; they either walk about like this or sit in a corner, suitably draped, whilst they doze. This is an inborn behaviour pattern. In the wild they habitually use the largest possible leaves to cover their nests, pull=ing the leaves down all round them. Observers have also reported that they have seen orang=utans which placed leaves on their thinly=haired pates against the midday sun. This is probably significant because the natives of other areas protect themselves against the sun in the same way.

The drive to build nests is innate in the anthropoid apes. When they are captive in zoos, of course, there is no need for nest=building, because when evening comes they move over to their sleeping quarters, which have assumed the functions of the nest. Nevertheless, the drive breaks out again if they can lay their hands on any material which they can use for nest=building. If this drive is assisted, by providing them with leafy branches, apes which previously have never seen how it is done start to build. This is what happened with Jenny, the chimpanzee, when her grooming instinct was stimulated by the puppy, and the carrier=bag — lying close at hand — presented itself as suitable nest=building material.

The Munster zoologist, Professor Bernhard Rensch, was able to observe the same behaviour in young chimpanzees in his Institute:

The chimp gathered together some branches, and sat down in the middle of them. Then he stood up again, seized a branch with his hand, bent it into a circle and trod on it with his feet. This he repeated several times. He revolved on his own axis and in this way he arrived at a round formation for the nest. In a few minutes the construction was finished.

One may well ask why the anthropoid apes build nests. Nest=building is scarcely a typical form of human behaviour. Or is it, perhaps, some kind of link or bridge? As we have seen, apes must build nests, it is in their blood. When an ape goes to sleep, it does not usually just sit on a branch or use a tree=trunk as a back=rest and squat down. Perhaps it needs a sense of security which only comes from having some kind of shelter around it. Do we humans also not feel something similar? Is it not true that we only feel really safe when we are unseen, safe within the four walls of our home? It is not such a big step from the nest of the apes to the human bedroom.

One day when I was in the habitat of the gorillas and chimpanzees I watched a family of pygmies building their leaf huts. As I watched them it struck me that they could well be "master" chimpanzees. As Adieta, the chief of the pygmy tribe, climbed a tree, doing a mime dance of a sudden attack by chimpanzees on the pygmies, I was tempted to assume that pygmies had evolved from chimpanzees or gorillas — even though this assumption is known to be incorrect. The striking resemblance of pygmies to apes, however, could well have led one astray. The pygmy, himself, feels very close to and respects the chimpanzee. He firmly believes, even today, that it was the chimpanzee who gave him fire. A very honoured pygmy name is therefore Assami, which means: an extraordinarily good chim= panzee.

Moritz, a young orang=utan in the collection of anthropoid apes at the Wilhelma Zoo, Stuttgart: Moritz frequently jumps on his keeper's back while his cage is being cleaned. He has just been told very firmly to keep out of the way. He pouts and grumbles in protest.

Anthropoid apes in captivity are always ready to steal a towel or cloth of any kind. This is not abnormal beha= viour but is part of their natural urge to build nests. There are no building mate= rials in a cage and so they try to get hold of any suit= able substitute. When they drape a towel over their heads, this gives them a feel= ing of security which would be fulfilled in the wild by building a nest.

The behaviour of a rhesus monkey when she found a paper bag containing a puppy at the foot of her cage, start= ed me off on a comparative study of the reactions of monkeys and man during the early years of anthropoid life, known as the "chimpan= zee age". I used in my ex= periments two boys, a girl and a female chimpanzee. Each one of them was pre= sented with a similiar situ= ation in which I put a large paper bag containing a pup= py in front of them. The results were astonishing. The two female "experimental animals" showed an extra= ordinary similarity in hand= ling the situation, whereas the two males had an empi= rical and individual approach, behaving quite differently from each other.

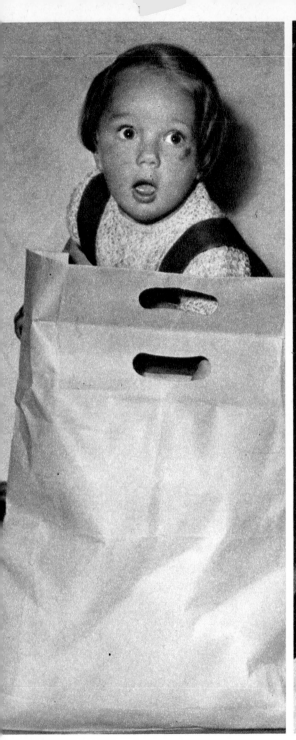

Parallel reactions: Barbi, the rhesus monkey, has just seen the puppy in the bag on the ground and she registers astonishment at her discovery. Several weeks later, Fritzi — a little girl aged $1^1/_2$ years — finds a puppy and registers her astonishment in a faithful reproduction of the monkey's facial expression. When I put a paper bag in front of Jenny, the chimpanzee, she reached into it in a precisely similar way to young Fritzi.

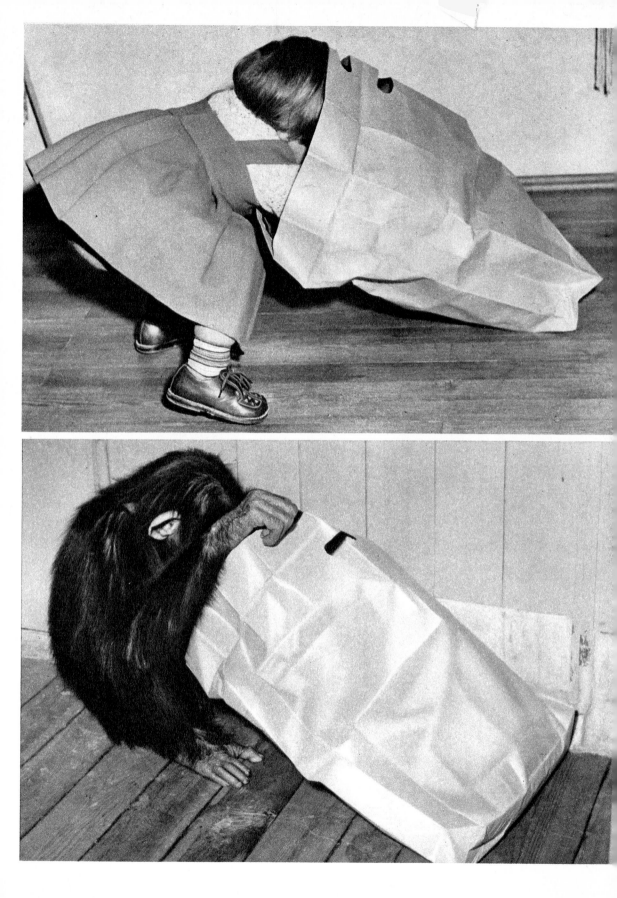

Jenny, a five=year=old chimpanzee at the Munich Hellabrunn Zoo: she found it too complicated to lift the puppy out of the bag, so she turned it over and hastily tore the paper. In this way she got to the puppy quickly. The next problem was how to get hold of it. The head was too bulky, so what could be more natural than to grab it by the tail? With this grip she can pull the puppy towards her quite conveniently; she senses its tender age and wants to nurse it.

22

Fritzi, one of my "experimental animals", in her nursery: she has never seen Jenny and does not know of the chimpanzee's method of gripping the puppy. Insight leads her to make use of the same grip. At $1^1/_2$ years of age her mental powers are hardly superior to those of the chimpanzee. Faced with the same situation she also wants to hold and fondle the puppy. The maternal instinct, dormant in both Fritzi and Jenny, is aroused by the helpless puppy.

An impressive dance by an angry chimpanzee has its parallel in an ape=exorcising dance

performed by pygmy tribes in central Africa in connection with hunting and ancestral rites.

It is natural for apes to build nests and Jenny, the chimpanzee, tries to make a nest for her puppy out of the remains of the paper bag used in my experiment.

The primitive human dwarfs of the Ituri Forest in the Congo build their leafhuts in a similar way to their neighbours the apes (below).

An "ape-man" visits a real ape. When I watched Fritz Roth give his performance as King-Kong in the circus, dressed in an ape costume with a detachable mask, I wondered how chimpanzees would behave when faced with this "human colleague". When he first appeared their reaction was flight. Mimi, keeping close to her keeper for protection, eventually approached the terrifying creature.

It was only when Roth re=
moved his mask that the
chimpanzee lost her fear. She
immediately recognized him
as a man and seemed quite
pleased. But she was still un=
easy and she kept hold of
her keeper while she tested
the stranger's new lips by
touching them with her
tongue. They were real lips.
Then she made a counter
check on the mask and for the
first time she seemed to relax.
She gave a triumphant shout,
calling out to the other apes
who were near and assuring
them that the man was
harmless (see pp. 31–33).

All the chimps now knew that the creature in the pelt was a man. Would they remember this if he put the mask on again while they watched? On the contrary, they rushed away from him with shrill screams, reacting to the change with headlong flight. He had become an unidentifiable monster whose lips gave them no information. Apes orientate primarily with their eyes. The senses of smell and taste confirm the visual impression. What they see at any particular moment is what counts and their visual impression determines their first reaction.

An orang=utan's laugh is extraordinarily human. There is no mistaking it and this makes it most ▶ attractive. All members of the ape family, however, do not laugh in the same way as humans. For example, if a chimp made a similar face to the orang shown in the picture opposite, it would indicate either that it was in pain or very angry. Chimpanzees laugh in quite a different way (see pp. 230–231).

CHAPTER 3

The Ape-man and the Anthropoid Apes

WHEN I WENT to the Paula Busch Circus I noticed that one of the acts in the pro=
gramme was referred to simply as "King Kong". The tamer of lions and tigers
finished his act with the customary bow and the audience applauded; the darkness
swallowed up the trainer of the big cats outside the arena and the ironwork of the
cage clattered as the dismantling started. Suddenly a dazzling spotlight picked out
a huge ape amongst the public, the audience shrieked as it leaped from bench to
bench and, before people realized what was really happening, the ape grabbed a
rope and shinned up into the dome of the tent where it performed incredible gym=
nastic feats, high above the crowd. The "ape", known as King Kong, was in real=
ity a man; he was only small in stature but he showed complete mastery of the
movements of anthropoid apes — just like the pygmies who live in the endless
forest regions of central Africa. In the star=studded bill of circus performers, King
Kong's act counted for little more than interval music, a fill=in to cover the dis=
mantling of the iron cage. The expertise of King Kong, however, started me on a
new train of thought about animal observation. In his act, the human King Kong
pretended to be an ape by donning a pelt and mask; his job was to use his skill
to attract the attention of the audience up into the roof of the arena until the dis=
mantling of the cage below was complete. Weightless, he twisted and turned,
flying through the air at dizzy heights — all this without a net — just as the apes
on which he had modelled his performance mastered the lianas of their natural
habitat. At the sound of a whistle he slid down the rope to the tan of the arena.
Off came his mask and the audience clapped enthusiastically. The applause was
well and truly earned. To all of us King Kong appeared to be a real ape.

"Excuse me a moment," I whispered to my wife, who was naturally puzzled
as I dashed out of the arena. I asked the ringmaster where I could find King Kong's
caravan and seconds later I was sitting opposite Fritz Roth, the athletic performer
from Ludwigshafen. The chimpanzee mask lay on the table and, with sweat pour=
ing off him, he immediately peeled off the restricting pelt. I put my question to
him: "Would you be prepared to go in amongst the chimpanzees at Hellabrunn
Ape Centre, wearing your mask and pelt?"

On the whole, Fritz Roth was not very enthusiastic about my idea. This man
who had just given such a courageous and carefree display admitted that he
would be scared to death. "It is true," he said, "that I have studied the anthro=

poid apes for a long time; I know all their typical movements, can mimic their voices and, as you have seen, can imitate them in a hundred and one different ways. But I also know all about the chimpanzee mentality and the unpredictability of adult apes. If I went amongst them in my costume and they got angry, I would be torn to pieces. I would also be very worried about my costume — it is hand= stitched and cost me a fortune. I am very sorry but it is definitely not on."

I asked Roth if he could tell precisely when chimpanzees would attack, but he replied that it would be impossible to be certain about this. I explained to him that for research purposes I was interested to find out what chimpanzees would do in such circumstances and that we had no experience of how they would react because, as far as I knew, no experiment of this kind had ever taken place. In the end I persuaded him to give the matter further consideration whilst I consulted the experts at the Munich Zoo.

The next day, after long and detailed negotiations, I got the reluctant approval of the Zoo authorities to my experiment. The experts were very sceptical and not at all clear as to how the experiment would turn out. This, of course, was what I found stimulating. Now that I had the approval of the senior officials, I only needed the advice and opinion of one other person: Alois, the keeper of the anthro= poid apes at Hellabrunn, was by no means the least important person to be con= sulted. For years Alois had been dealing with the apes, day in day out. He had bred nearly all of them; he knew each one personally, knew their individual characters, and had something to say to each one of them — in fact he was their "leading ape". It was quite obvious that my experiment could never take place without his consent, and official permission was worthless without the keeper's backing.

I soon worked things out with Alois. I was surprised how little opposition he raised but his position with the apes was so secure that even if one of them should dare to attack Fritz Roth, it was clear that Alois would have no difficulty in get= ting the troop under control. Nevertheless, I hoped that this would not be neces= sary because if Alois stifled an attack at birth I should get no photographs. I made a private agreement with Alois, which we did not divulge to the ape=man, that he would only intervene at the last moment in the event of an attack.

After much discussion with Alois, Fritz Roth agreed to take part in the experi= ment, albeit with some anxiety. I was decidedly relieved: the experiment was on and we decided that it should take place the following morning. I must confess that I spent a restless night, wondering — like a child on Christmas Eve — what the morning would bring: would the apes see through the masquerade imme= diately? Would they "nose out" the man in spite of his disguise, recognizing him perhaps by his movements? They might even attack him immediately, seeking to drive the stranger out of their territory.

At an early hour I set up my camera in front of the chimpanzees' open enclo= sure. There were five apes in the enclosure; none was more than seven years old and this in itself provided a certain amount of security for Fritz Roth. Apes which are sexually immature will respect their leader, and in an emergency they would follow Alois and not get out of control. None of us would have dared to risk the experiment with adult male chimpanzees. As the other people gathered to watch the experiment, I became tense with excitement. In addition to the Direc= tor and his assistants there were several people who were interested in animal behaviour, amongst them Paul Eipper, the well=known writer on animals. We approached the enclosure like ordinary members of the public.

We had arranged that King Kong should change into his costume in the inner cage, unnoticed by the chimps, but we had reckoned without the animals' ability to sense the unusual. As we arrived, the apes were having their breakfast but they were not behaving quite naturally, they were restless and fidgety; they looked round all the time and kept eyeing the ape=house — they were not concen= trating. Chimpanzees are normally volatile, quick to seize on anything new, never sticking to anything for very long. But the restlessness which they showed on this particular morning was, in my experience, above average. I wondered if they were already aware that something out of the normal daily routine was going on in the inner cage. We were all suffering from nervous strain and the tension must have been in the atmosphere.

We do not know, generally speaking, to what extent animals are capable of reasoning, that is, to what extent they relate mysterious happenings and interpret them. In acquiring culture man has become too obtuse to share the feelings of animals, he can only observe their reactions. We noticed that it was not only the apes in our enclosure which were restless; in the more remote sections, the adult apes were nervously excited and there was unrest throughout the whole centre.

The iron door of the cage clicked softly. With a small jump, the ape=man landed on all fours in the sandy enclosure. The apes left their places at the table in great haste. Apples, bananas, oranges, lettuces all went flying and for a moment there was panic. Then there was a single sharp scream. All the apes had screamed simultaneously and this was the prelude to an infernal noise. Piercing shrieks rent the air. A respectful distance lay between the ape=man and the chimpanzees. The youngest animals hid themselves, trembling, behind Alois; the two seven= year olds fled to the roof of the pavilion. At the rear, the adult apes rattled iron bars, screamed and stamped their feet. They were seething with rage, driven to fury by their powerlessness to attack the stranger in their territory. They goaded the younger ones and it was as though they were saying "Go on, you little cowards, chuck him out." The effect of this vocal incitement was stupefying. By this time Mimi and Maxl, the two seven=year olds, were yelling in a frenzied soprano from the roof of the pavilion; with their hair standing on end, they beat their breasts with their fists and stamped on the wood of the climbing frame so that it reverberated — the pandemonium was scarcely tolerable to human ears.

King Kong took three leaps and landed on the breakfast table. The chimpanzees did not attack. After their first panic=stricken flight from the strange creature they began to accept its presence. When their screams started to die down, the old guard from the other cages spurred them on again. But the young animals still kept the same distance and, in spite of the incitement of the older apes, they refused to reduce the gap by even an inch. The two bigger apes continued to trample on the roof while the youngsters sought maximum safety from danger by staying close to their leader, Alois. It was a touching demonstration of the intimate relationship between man and animal. Helga, the youngest and therefore the most worried, had immediately jumped up into Alois' arms at the approach of the unknown; Moni and Schorschl, the other two, had huddled together, taking cover behind Alois. There they remained and continued to scream shrilly.

Now and again the anger of the older apes burst out afresh but while Fritz Roth remained squatting on the table it was only echoed feebly. The ape=man sat quietly for a time and then, with an ape=like movement, he stretched out his right hand towards Alois. Reaction was immediate: the screaming stopped dead. The animals on the platform looked anxious but displayed curiosity. Alois moved very cau= tiously forward with his "children", reassuring them with his voice as step by step he approached the "unknown". It was a singular picture, one that made a deep impression on me. The chimpanzees showed complete trust and confidence by their gestures; their boss was with them and so nothing could go wrong. Helga crouched under his arm, Moni showed a certain amount of curiosity but sought protection by clinging to the keeper's leg, and Schorschl, also pressing closely against Alois, stared anxiously at the rigid mask on the face of the "unknown". King Kong made no sound. We had previously agreed that he should remain silent throughout the experiment as I wanted to give the apes as little chance as possible to adapt themselves too quickly.

The pelt costume of the ape=man smelt a little of mothballs and also of human sweat. Even my insensitive human nose noticed this and I wondered how this smell struck the apes for the first time. They would not know how to interpret the scent they received. They were distinctly uneasy, turning first one way and then another, continually looking questioningly at Alois. But the keeper quietly reiterated: "Schorschl! Moni! There's no need to worry, he won't do anything to us." Naturally the apes did not understand the words he used but this did not matter. It was the tone of his voice that they understood. Their sense of smell told them that the creature was not an ape. It smelt rather like a human but it did not look like one.

Alois had never let Mimi and Maxl, the two larger apes, out of his sight. As he approached within reach of the "unknown", Mimi and Maxl were hanging from the roof, their hair still standing on end, their nerves on edge. Suddenly Mimi let out a shrill scream and rushed forward to attack. Alois intervened like lightning. This could very easily have turned out nastily. I heard King Kong breathe heavily under his costume. Moni and Schorschl had seized the opportunity to flee from the proximity of the weird stranger. Only Helga remained in the keeper's arms as he called to the big ape: "Mimi, don't be so cross, come on now; come here, Mimi, come on!" Cautiously he approached the strong female. She climbed up the keep=

er's leather trousers, pulled herself up and then sat down very carefully on the extreme edge of the table. She stared steadfastly at the "dead" mask. A face with= out movement was something which did not exist in her experience. It was obvious to me that she wanted to explore the papier=mâché lips. Mouth and lips are expres= sive of the state of mind of their owner both in apes and humans. Chimpanzees know this but Mimi was not sure if this would apply. She tried to appear friendly towards the big creature by shaping her lips like those on the mask. Then she waited: nothing moved in the face opposite. This increased her curiosity and she held out her index finger tentatively towards the mask. Mimi wanted to stick her finger into the mouth of the mask. For the sake of safety, Alois' arm accompanied Mimi's movement. Her fingertips felt the cold, rigid papier=mâché. Once again I saw the chimp stiffen all over.

It was quite obvious to me that anxiety was building up again in the chim= panzees and I decided that we had enough of the gruesome game and I called out to Fritz Roth to remove his mask.

Mimi voiced her amazement. "Hu=hu=hu=hu!" She jumped right on to the table and gripped Alois round the shoulder, apparently with relief, as though she were saying "Look, it's a man, I knew it was." Then without any hesitation she went right up to Fritz Roth. Her anxieties were gone and her curiosity was aroused. Now she investigated everything: first, of course, the lips — the strongest medium of expression for a chimp — which she had previously found so constricted and disappointing. She examined the man's lips with her long tongue and was very pleased with the results: everything was warm and soft. Next she abandoned Roth's face and looked around as though searching for something. I realized then what Mimi was looking for: the papier=mâché mask. She tested it; its rigid cold= ness held no interest for her and she laid it aside. She returned quickly to the man, put her arm round him and sniffed his neck and ears. She looked at his pelt and seemed to be considering whether to "de=louse" it, but something appeared to hold her back.

While Mimi had been investigating Fritz Roth, young Helga had jumped down from the keeper's arms and she now became inquisitive. Together with Moni and Schorschl she suddenly came on to the scene. The three youngsters stood below the table. "Hu=hu=hu!" said Mimi and seized the ape=man's chin, turning it towards Moni. She turned his face in all directions and repeatedly stuck her forefinger into Roth's mouth. Through this action she made the others understand that there was nothing to fear. The youngsters approached hesitantly and then sprang on the table and, putting their arms round the man, they pressed their faces into his artificial pelt.

I then decided to see what would happen if Fritz Roth put his mask on again. He slowly disengaged himself from the arms of the chimpanzees and carefully picked up his mask. As soon as the apes saw the man grasp the mask, they immediately retreated and sought protection from their leader Alois. Did they sense a change? They never took their eyes off Fritz Roth, watching intently every move that he made. Next he jammed the papier=mâché skull over his head but a large tuft of hair remained over the face of the mask. Mimi's eyes widened anxiously and her excitement showed in the pouting of her lips. Then Fritz Roth brushed the hair back from the mask. The chimpanzees were horrified by the movement. Only the mask had any significance, everything else was forgotten. Fear and terror engulfed the chimpanzees. Alois was almost knocked over and once again shrill screams filled the air. King Kong went down on his knees but the chimpanzees had only one idea — to get right away.

"Enough, Herr Roth, thank you," I called. With obvious relief the ape=man hopped back into the inner room and shut the cage door behind him. . . . The apes hurried over, pressed their noses between the bars and stared and stared.

I packed up my camera. I had been able to record almost every stage in the experiment. I have seldom been so moved by the expressions on the faces of the apes. For no apparent reason I suddenly thought of Christmas Eve — even though it was midsummer. It was the immobility of King Kong's mask that made me think of it. When I was small, Father Christmas always had the same kind of rigid ex= pression above his long white beard. His face never moved even when he scolded me: "If you don't eat, young man, you'll die." When I howled with fright, every= one tried to comfort me by saying it was only my grandfather. He would then remove his mask: "Now just watch," he would say, as he put the mask on again. But it made me scream all over again, and this is why my memories of Father Christmas are not altogether pleasant. I believe that the chimpanzees went through much the same kind of experience with King Kong; they were frightened although they had seen there was a man beneath the mask.

Visual information is highly significant in young chimpanzees. What they see at any one moment carries more weight with them than any experience from memory, however recent, and where the visual contradicts what seems to be appa= rent, the visual impression is dominant.

CHAPTER 4

Mr Walther — the Buck Gazelle

ONE SPRING EVENING there were still many visitors entering the gates of the Kronberg Reserve for Animal Research as the shadows lengthened. They spent some time watching the elephants, they admired the agility of the ibex and the speed of the blackbuck, and they even enjoyed having water blown at them by the two huge hippos, George and Augusta. Then, in a large paddock reserved for animals of the African savannahs, they saw a bewildering sight: a herd of graceful, long-limbed gazelles were making their way towards a shed and in amongst them, crawling on all fours, was a man. A few minutes earlier he had been lying down on the ground, tugging at the green grass as though cropping it like a gazelle; every now and again one of the gazelles would come up to rub noses with him. It was such an extraordinary sight that the visitors wondered if the man could be quite right in the head. Wondering what could possibly be going on, the visitors sat down on a bank to watch.

The Reserve was not far from the busy airport of Rhein-Main, and high overhead screaming jet aircraft left white trails of condensation in the blue sky. The ruined tower of Falkenstein was sharply silhouetted on the skyline and a fresh breeze blew down the valley from the Taunus Mountains. The visitors felt the chill of the evening as they sat waiting for the man to reappear. Little did they know that it would be dawn before Mr Walther emerged once again into the paddock.

Fritz Rudolf Walther is a zoologist who studies animal behaviour — he is also the scientific director of the Reserve. His special interest is in cattle and antelopes. Ever since Professor Konrad Lorenz confirmed that little was known about this fascinating group of animals, Walther has pursued his studies and observations with remarkable intensity.

At this time his research was centred principally on the Dorcas gazelle, that graceful inhabitant of the deserts of north Africa and northern Arabia, where it ranges from Morocco through Algeria and Libya to Syria and southward to northern Sudan. The Dorcas is smaller and more ornamental than the European roe deer, and like the soil of Africa it is sandy reddish-brown in colour. Its flanks are marked with a striking black longitudinal stripe which contrasts sharply with the white belly. Both sexes carry lyre-shaped ringed horns. The Dorcas is the gazelle of the classics.

In order to learn more about the behaviour of the gazelles, their language and method of communicating with one another, Walther decided that it was necessary to spend some time actually living with the gazelles as a member of the herd. He considered that he could hear and see much more if he lived as a gazelle among gazelles. He therefore decided to make himself small and go down on all fours to join the herd; and this method of study made it imperative that he should sleep with them.

Before long Walther ceased to be regarded as a strange human being by his animals and whenever he approached them they accepted him quickly. They treated him as a gazelle buck and, as his physique was more powerful than that of his more delicately built companions, they regarded him as an "alpha animal" — in other words, as their leader. The gazelles became completely unconcerned at his close proximity, and this, of course, was exactly what he had hoped for in order to carry out his research.

At first all went well. He found that standing shoulder to shoulder with them he was accepted freely as a member of the herd and could observe every action and ritual of these decorative quadrupeds without disturbing them. They even greeted him in their own way, nudging him with their muzzles, rubbing noses and nibbling his lips with their own. He was accepted when shoulder to shoulder with them, but if he crawled up to them when they were already lying down and resting, hoping to squat amongst them, they stood up immediately and moved off, settling down again elsewhere.

It was clear that the human gazelle was behaving incorrectly. The zoologist still had to learn the gazelle "code of behaviour". Eagerly the uneducated buck gazelle studied his companions. He noticed that they often rested back to back with their heads facing outwards in different directions. This is known as the "star formation" to naturalists. It enables animals to widen their own field of vision and hearing, providing greater security from surprise attack on the open plains.

Walther wondered if it was breaking the rules to approach them face on and decided to try approaching them from the other side. Sure enough, they remained where they were and did not get up. (Moral: don't approach a resting gazelle from the front.) He found that there was one other rule to be observed before he could become part of the star formation: when he was one body's length away from the animals, it was necessary for him to turn round and move in backwards for the last yard and a half until his rear touched their hind-quarters. They tolerated this method of approach and the human gazelle could then rest with the animals, each one of them facing outwards and looking in all directions for mutual protection.

This formation is typical of many horned ungulates when they are resting. At first scientists thought that it was an inborn behaviour pattern but Walther's intensive observations have thrown rather a different light on this theory. He explained it to me thus: when animals, both old and young, lie down together, they often try to lean against each other; their hind=quarters touch and their fore=quarters diverge at angles of up to 180°, in a star formation. The purpose of this orien= tation is obvious since it increases the field of vision, and this form of behaviour is commonly adopted when animals are liable to disturbance from a number of unknown directions; it could, therefore, be interpreted as an inborn behaviour pattern originating from the necessity to detect enemies.

But according to Walther, this is not the case: he observed that young animals seldom lie close to an adult or older juvenile in star formation, or if they do so it is only by accident; they endeavour to make bodily contact, preferably crouching immediately below the mother's nose in an attempt to nestle against her neck and breast, lying at right angles to her fore=quarters. When the young animals approach other adults in this way, they are immediately rebuffed; the adult thrusts the fawn away, the fawn turns its head and steps aside with its forelegs to avoid the blows thus coming near the flanks of the adult, where the fawn continues to strive for bodily contact, pressing close to the adult's side. This method of approach is acceptable, and once this has happened several times the young animal lies down orientated in the star formation, close to its companion.

The star formation is, therefore, not an innate behaviour pattern originating from the need to detect enemies but the result of a compromise between two res= ponses: on the one hand the young animal shows a strong inclination to make bodily contact with an older companion and on the other hand the older animal resists a frontal approach.

The observation of this everyday performance immediately led Walther into difficult psychological problems. All at once he saw that the origin of a behaviour pattern may have nothing to do with its later function, even though it may have survival value. One question followed another. What, for instance, does inborn really mean? Although Walther knew for certain that the enemy=detecting star formation was not primarily inborn, he wondered why a gazelle should object to being approached from the front. Could it be that the experience of one gene= ration, in finding the best method of locating predators, is passed on from one generation to another? Although an inborn behaviour pattern might not function during the first few weeks of life, might it not become active when the animal has reached a certain degree of maturity? How long, in general, does the innate remain crystal=clear? And as Walther pondered these questions he knew that the layman would be wondering whether it was worth finding out the answer, even if it could be done.

A scientist can rarely predict what practical benefits will result from his research. When Otto Hahn and his co=workers split uranium and thorium, they did not foresee the consequences, and a hundred years ago Gregor Mendel did not realize that in his work on garden peas he was laying the foundations of modern genetics.

As a zoologist, however, Fritz Walther was certain of one thing: if we now have a science dealing with animals it is essential that we should study the be=

haviour of these animals with as much accuracy as we study their skeletons and distribution. It is regrettable that up to about forty years ago very little work was done on behaviour and we now have a whole series of animals which are faced with extinction. At the worst, if extinction does come to an animal, its bones, skin, skeleton and internal organs can still be studied; but research on behaviour must be done when the animal is still living. If we fail to make observations immediately on such threatened species, the opportunity will have gone for ever.

I had naturally hoped to photograph the human gazelle lying asleep with the herd at night but the animals were too nervous to permit this. I was able, however, to spend the whole day with the Dorcas herd. In the morning Walther left the shed with his animals as they moved out into the paddock to graze. The buck gazelles obviously took great delight in challenging the human buck to a little horn play but Walther always seemed to know how to withdraw tactfully. After the gazelles had trotted about the spacious paddock for some time, they came back to their slow=moving leader and greeted the human buck, either singly or in pairs, by rub= bing noses with him.

Fritz Walther also gave me the opportunity to photograph some aspects of the gazelle "code of behaviour". As we know, Dorcas gazelles regard the frontal approach as impolite but it was remarkably interesting to see the reaction of a resting buck to the approach of the human buck in this fashion. It stood up imme= diately, turned its back as though disgusted by such ill=mannered behaviour and moved off to lie down elsewhere. Next I watched the human buck approach from behind and the animal allowed him to crawl up very close, showing no sign of fear, until they were touching back to back.

The animal which took part in this demonstration was a one=horned buck which had unfortunately lost the other horn in an accident. This buck was named Sput= nik from the speed of his attacks in the days when he had a full complement of horns and was an acknowledged leader of the herd. As a result of losing one horn, sparring with other bucks was painful and the young bucks soon noticed that their leader avoided encounters. Sputnik was then "down=graded" from leader of the herd to the lowest ranks. When he went to the feeding=trough he always had to choose a time when the other animals were resting. In spite of this he was not allowed to feed in peace for long as the others appeared to begrudge him the food and quickly drove off their previous leader.

Walther had already established a good relationship with Sputnik before the accident to his horn and afterwards Sputnik clung even closer to him. The human buck was able to make particularly interesting observations on courtship display when the buck gazelle applied the whole gamut of its leg language to Walther himself.

I had been interested in this language of the leg for some time and was anxious to photograph it in all its phases. On this occasion, however, the buck showed no sexual responsiveness to Fritz Walther and so I gave him my camera and offered myself to Sputnik. By this time Sputnik knew me quite well and I too failed to excite him. As luck would have it my youngest son was with me and somewhat reluctantly he agreed to become a guinea=pig for the experiment. Sput= nik started to show intense interest in him as soon as he entered the paddock, raising his head and inflating his nasal pouches.

Whenever a stranger entered his paddock, Sputnik wanted to know whether it was male or female: was it a potential rival or a prospective mate? Walther had observed the courtship ritual on many occasions and knew the sequence of events inside out. Photography of this ritual had always proved unsatisfactory, partly because it cannot be initiated at will, but also because once it starts the action takes place very fast and spreads out over too wide an area for the photographer to keep up with the tempo. Sputnik and my son Volker were, however, a con= venient pair as far as I was concerned.

Sputnik behaved strictly according to the gazelle code of behaviour. He first nudged the stranger with his muzzle. This aroused no response from the human and the buck reacted by tapping the stranger's foot with one of his own small hooves. There was still no response and so the buck gazelle became a little rougher and tapped the stranger's legs with its own front legs — first with the right leg, then the left and so on. The buck then began to press forward against the human body with its head held high and its neck outstretched. The buck continued to press harder, thrusting its neck and head against the human body and pounding with its forelegs in the process. It was as though Sputnik were practising the tradi= tional Prussian goose=step against Volker. Sputnik's neck and head were raised higher and higher until he became perpendicular and the blows from his forelegs hurt my son's knees, but Volker did not give any ground. At this stage the buck gazelle was forced to come to a decision, for he had used up the whole of the ex= ploratory technique. If Sputnik could not get the stranger to give way, then ac= cording to the gazelle code the stranger must be a male and consequently a rival in his territory. Naturally a rival male must be chased off or reduced to an inferior social position and in such a case the buck must attack.

Sputnik started to use his single horn. At this point my son began to give way and took a step backwards. Sputnik appeared jubilant: a female after all! Sputnik continued to press the attack but Volker stood his ground. At once the buck react= ed, climbing up against Volkers' body and hammering away with both forelegs. The sexual drive had really become aroused. Sputnik's actions became more and more vigorous, the tempo increased and my son moved forward, as though to get away. This was the natural reaction for which Sputnik had worked: a wife must run away. Had Volker remained stationary, the buck would have renewed his pummel= ling. The gazelle code of behaviour lays it down that the marriage ceremony requires the buck to stimulate the female more and more until they finally mate.

Many of the visitors who went to the Kronberg Reserve were doubtless delighted by the sight of various animals living under comparatively natural conditions. Few of them, however, would be aware of the interesting research work being done with these animals. To study the behaviour of an animal it is necessary to have infinite patience and not everyone has the ability to understand animals. It requires imagination as well as skill to learn the code of behaviour of an animal and to live with it on terms of intimacy such as those adopted by Herr Walther. To the layman a scientist often appears to be doing something slightly ridiculous, but at an animal behaviour research station one learns never to be surprised by the behaviour of the humans.

CHAPTER 5

The Quadruped

I KNOW ANOTHER scientist who also went down on all fours in order to get closer to the animals which he was studying. But the reaction he obtained from his animals was quite different from that elicited by Fritz Walther from his gazelles. This scientist — named Klaus Zeeb — is a young veterinary surgeon at the Institute of Animal Hygiene at Freiburg University. He is a keen student of animal behaviour and one might almost describe him as a man with horse=sense. The title of his doctoral thesis at Munich was "The Behaviour of the Horse when En= countering Man". The subject of his thesis would have intrigued me even if I had not previously met Klaus Zeeb and known of his work. We often intended to go shooting together, but for years our plans had been thwarted by the demands of our different professions.

However, one summer day everything seemed to fit in and I collected Dr Zeeb from Stuttgart in my car. Our objective was Dülmen in Westphalia. We wanted to pay a visit to the Duke of Croy's wild horses, which live in the Merfelder Marsh. The young vet wanted to show me something special in connection with these horses; his seniors at headquarters kindly gave permission and so we set off one lovely morning and headed north along the autobahn.

It was a long drive and I listened with interest while Dr Zeeb talked about his observations on these primitive horses which live wild on the Dülmen hunting= chase. After spending countless hours watching a big herd through field=glasses he found, as time went on, that he tired more and more quickly; however good the binoculars, in the long run the image swam before his eyes; the task not only became irksome, his observations became inaccurate. For these particular studies it was important that the horses should be unaware of his presence and Dr Zeeb explained to me that the distance from which the observations could be made varied according to the time of the year, depending on the number of visits made by people to the hunting ground and the horses becoming accustomed to the pre= sence of humans. The distance varied between fifty and a hundred and fifty yards and observations were not easy at this distance, particularly when one individual horse had to be followed. Dr Zeeb explained that he could have got much nearer to the herd because the "withdrawal distance" — a fixed variant of the "flight dis= tance" — is approximately three yards and pretty constant for Dülmen horses. But although the Dülmen horses would have tolerated him at closer quarters, his visible presence would have influenced the behaviour of the herd in one way or another and thus his observations would have been valueless had he gone closer.

Dr Zeeb then told me of an idea he had for getting better results more quickly. He decided to get as near the herd as possible by crawling towards them. "No sooner thought of than done," he said. "While out of sight of the herd, I got down on all fours; then I moved over the ground as unobtrusively as possible, crawling and wriggling along — just like stalking game. I found that by this method I could get to about sixty yards from the herd but no nearer. At this distance the ponies' heads went up, they were immediately on the alert; I went on moving in towards them, but they snorted and fled. By this time I was puffing and blowing so much that I decided to have a rest; the horses had gone, so I sat down and cursed. You try running two hundred yards on all fours some time; I am still young but it certainly took the stuffing out of me!"

Dr Zeeb's first attempt at crawling resulted in the flight of the herd and while he was getting his breath back he thought the matter over. There was no doubt in his mind that when walking normally, in an upright position, he got considerably closer to the herd than when he approached them crawling on all fours. He decided to try the experiment again. He made a fresh approach to the herd, once again on all fours. The result was the same — another failure. What did it all mean? The Dülmen horses certainly posed a problem and it occurred to Zeeb that it would be interesting to find out if other horses would react in such a singular manner to what he called his quadruped test. He decided to make a virtue out of necessity and use his unsuccessful experiment as a subject for research. He travelled far and wide, applying his quadruped test to the wild horses of the Camargue in the south of France, to Exmoor ponies in England, to the Arabian horses in the Hellabrunn Zoo at Munich. All these horses gave the same reaction. "It all seemed to fit so nicely," he said, "and as you know, we scientists are always longing for patterns and rules; but there was one thing that did not fit, one kind of horse which fell right outside what I had come to regard as the normal reaction to the quadruped test. And this was the Shetland pony. On every occasion that I approached Shetland ponies by the crawling method, there was no sign of flight — on the contrary, the ponies appeared to regard me as a friendly human being. I got the same reaction from this race whether the Shetland ponies were in England, Scotland or in a German zoo. On each occasion my method of approach was treated as quite normal. I wondered, of course, what was the significance of this difference in reaction from that of other horses."

It was obvious to me that Klaus Zeeb had given a lot of thought to the whole meaning of what he called his quadruped test. I asked him how he interpreted his results. "In my opinion it is an innate behaviour pattern for protection against predators which are in the same size range as a human on all fours. I am inclined to see in it," he said, "an inborn fear of wolves and bears. This would also explain the behaviour of the Shetland pony; this race could not possibly have such an inborn fear because these predatory animals have never existed in the Shetland Isles.''

At Recklinghausen I left the autobahn and took the route to Münster and half an hour later we were driving down the main street of Dülmen. By then it was late afternoon and it was the last Saturday in May. It was precisely twenty=five years since I had last paid a visit to this small Westphalian town. Then, as now, it was horses which had brought me here.

The last Saturday in May is the one day in the year on which the mass of the herd — excluding the adult stallions — are rounded up and brought into close con= tact with man for a few hours. Normally these horses never come near a stable, summer or winter, and live completely free and wild. This round=up of wild horses is unique in Germany and people come from far and wide. There is a public auction and the young stallions are much in demand but, quite apart from busi= ness reasons, many people come as sightseers and it is a public festival for young and old. The Duke of Croy has made a large corral so that as many people as possible can enjoy the spectacle.

First of all the whole herd including the foals — usually over two hundred ani= mals — is driven into the arena. The mares with their unweaned foals are then allowed to escape, leaving the yearling stallions in the arena. Tough, daring young men then fling themselves on the animals, using only their bare hands to throw the horses and to force their heads into rope halters. The animals kick and struggle but when they are sufficiently subdued they are branded with the ducal arms and then auctioned.

There is nothing refined about catching a stallion, it requires brute strength and as soon as one suggests the use of force some people get angry. Nevertheless cer= tain facts have to be faced. Wherever man and animals meet on earth, conflicts arise and these result in nearly every case in the defeat of the animal either psych= ologically or physically. With the exception of the cat, our domesticated animals cannot escape this fate. If we do not eat them at some time or another, we force them to live with us.

In the case of the Dülmen horses the removal of the young stallions is essential for reasons of husbandry as well as for breeding purposes. The acreage of the chase will support only a certain number of animals. The herd is split up after the male yearlings have been caught and the stallions are then allowed to run with the mares again. The herd is only disturbed once a year and the young ani= mals soon recover from the shock of being rounded up and manhandled. In pro= fessional circles the Dülmen breed is very much in demand. They are naturally hardy through living in a wild state. Noted for their endurance and strength, they also have an equable temperament which is legendary.

I was anxious to photograph Klaus Zeeb's quadruped test being put into action and I returned to Dülmen on 18 June, when the herds were once again running free over Merfelder Marsh. One of my rules for photographing large assemblies of animals is to get up as high as possible. Without adequate height it is very

difficult to give the impression of a mass of animals on one photograph. To illus=
trate the quadruped test, it was particularly important to show the herd of animals
in relation to Klaus Zeeb — on all fours — in the one picture. A marsh, however,
is not exactly full of trees and bushes suitable for making into a flat but lofty
perch and I wondered whether to get a tall hide built specially for the purpose.
The difficulty lay in deciding where to build it, since there was no way of know=
ing in advance where the herds would be at the start of the experiment. It would
have meant building a number of tall hides in several different places on the marsh.

Klaus Zeeb then had a brilliant idea which was really very simple. On the day
of the round=up he had noticed cars being directed to parking places by the Dül=
men police who used a "Giraffe" as a mobile traffic=control tower. If I could pro=
cure a machine of the type kept by municipal authorities for repairing overhead
equipment and tall structures, it would be the solution to all my problems. Fortun=
ately there was a "Giraffe" factory quite close to Dülmen. The machines were
constructed on the principle of steel tubes fitted into one another which could be
drawn in or out by changes in air or oil pressure; the tubes supported a small
crow's=nest platform which was raised or lowered rather like a telescope.

The beauty of the machine was that I could work it singlehanded without hav=
ing to shout instructions down to anyone on the ground. By means of two press
buttons and levers I could raise myself forty=five feet above the ground. This was
equivalent in height to a four=storey building and was really excellent. We called
the machine "Giraffe" because, with its long thin neck supporting the crow's nest
at the end like a small head, it looked remarkably like these bizarre African ani=
mals. In addition the long steel neck fulfilled the same function for me as the real
neck did for the giraffes: it provided an observation post which gave me the widest
possible view. And so, in the early hours of one morning, we drove our monster
on to Merfelder Marsh and selected an unobtrusive position on the edge of a
large plain amongst a belt of tall trees. The "Giraffe" had conspicuous red and
white stripes which might well have aroused the suspicion of the wild horses and
so I camouflaged it with a lot of old sacks. Then, after a final demonstration from
the experts, I soared up on my first trial lift.

The early morning wind was decidedly gusty. I was about forty feet up in the
air and my observation post plunged about like a rebellious horse; I had the ridi=
culous feeling that I was about to lose my balance at any minute and tip right
over. This feeling was particularly strong each time I leaned over the side and
looked down. Far below me, the chassis of the lorry which formed the base of
the swaying structure looked very small indeed and I felt rather helpless. It would
obviously take time to get used to this new position between heaven and earth

A newly born Dorcas gazelle, not yet ten hours old, lies waiting for its mother to call it out for
a meal. Young gazelles are not suckled in the same place that they use for resting.

The gazelle of the classics: for thousands of years the Dorcas gazelle has been the symbol of weightless elegance. The gazelles' natural home is in the deserts of Arabia and Africa but their supple grace and agile beauty have made them an inspiration to poets and artists all over the world. A scientist, Fritz Walther, also fell for their charms and made them the focal point of his research. Little is known about their behaviour but amongst other things he observed that it is regarded as bad manners to approach a gazelle from the front when it is resting. It will tolerate an approach from the rear because this is the way in which one Dorcas gazelle approaches another (picture opposite). Like other horned animals they often rest in "star formation" (colour picture above), thus enlarging the field of vision.

54

A gazelle which makes close contact with a human is behaving abnormally as a result of being kept in captivity. Sputnik, a one=horned tame buck, is testing a visitor with his legs. The zoologist watches the movements of the buck, which are inborn. The actions are part of the courtship ritual of the Dorcas gazelle, which starts with the buck's rapping the hooves of his forelegs to indicate to the female that he intends to drive her.

The visitor retreats rather than engage in a struggle with Sputnik, who knows how to use his one horn in a fight. The man's retreat is more than welcome as far as the buck is concerned because it stimulates his growing ardour. He pursues the stranger and, when the latter stands still, the buck raps him continually with his forelegs until the man withdraws, thus stimulating the buck still further. It is part of the courtship ritual of the Dorcas gazelle that the female should run faster and faster from the buck until he finally catches up with her.

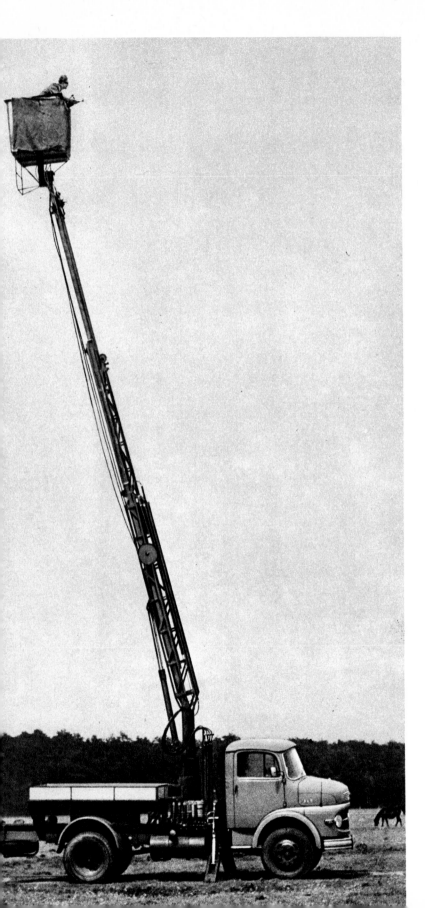

Forty feet up with the camera on the "Giraffe", overlook= ing the herd of wild horses on the Merfelder Marsh. I have been recommending amateur photographers for a long time to take pictures of crowds from an elevated position — one can scarcely convey the impression of a crowd from the angle of a frog's eye. This is all right in theory and a high angle is easily obtained for human crowds. There are places, such as heath and moorland, where there is no possibility of gaining any height. When photographing the Duke of Croy's herd of wild horses, I was able to hire a self= operating elevator, mounted on a modern truck, of the type used in fire=fighting and in other municipal work.

Germany's most primitive horse: these horses are known as the "Dülmen wild horses" in spite of the fact that their manes hang down, that they have forelocks and are of various colours — all of them undesirable characteristics in the breeding and domestication of truly wild horses. Never= theless they live wild on the moorland, heath and in virgin forest in Westphalia just as their ancestors did. They are the only direct descendants of the true wild horse in Europe. The herd numbers 200. It lives in the 500=acre reserve and, except in the depths of winter, the horses are never fed and no vet ever attends them.

Every year on the last Saturday of the month of May the same exciting event takes place in the reserve at twilight: the stallion returns to the herd. For nine months in the year he is kept apart from the mares for breeding reasons. His return takes place after the round=up of the young stallions. He is led to the reserve, his halter is removed and he then gallops at full speed towards the herd. His neigh becomes a scream, carrying far and wide over the reserve, and it is echoed by many in the herd. The mares with foals get out of the way of the urgent summons. The mating drive is strong in him, he paws the ground and blows at the mares, his nostrils distended.

63

It was on the Merfelder Marsh that the young behaviour scientist Dr Klaus Zeeb made a remark=
able discovery. When he tried approaching the horses on all fours, in order to get nearer for
convenient observation, he found that the herd scattered and showed every sign of fear. If he
stayed on all fours the herd remained on the alert. But, if he walked upright like a normal human
being, he found that he could get right up to them, close enough to touch them. After numerous
controlled experiments on widely varying races of horses throughout Europe, Dr Zeeb came
to the conclusion that the old fear of predators is deeply ingrained in the horse. Another point
which was apparent: the leading stallion of the present=day herd, like his ancestors, takes command
of the whole herd when some special danger threatens.

65

The Dülmen foals nibble one another's coats, mostly on the back in places which they cannot reach on themselves. Thirty colts and about the same number of fillies see the light of day every year on the Merfelder Marsh. Life is harsh for the young foals. Natural selection works ruth=lessly and only the strong survive.

A shaft of light through the trees silhouettes a giant, mouse=grey index finger. The wild stallion ▶ Nimbus wrinkles his nose and opens his mouth, taking the scent of his mares.

The fight of the stallions: at Achental, near the Chiemsee in Bavaria, two hostile stallions meet in an enclosure surrounded by a high fence. Kaid (left) and Raschid (right) are both sons of the Arab stallion Vishnu. The encounter between them was arranged so that I could photograph the early stages of a fight between stallions for the first time. The fight was by no means limited to biting. Both fought savagely for the supremacy of the herd.

The two Arab stallions do not rush at each other. There is a ritual to be observed. Kaid struts about as he challenges Raschid. Raschid ignores him and goes through the motions of grazing, placing himself at an angle to Kaid (above left). Both point their muzzles in opposite directions. They mark the ground for the take=off by defaecating. Kaid rears up, neighing. Raschid grazes again. The two stallions then back on to each other. Action will start soon.

Wild horses in the Merfelder Marsh. Dülmen mares are not for sale.

◀ The duel between the stallions reaches its climax with circling pirouettes and the exchange of thunderous blows. The combatants scream as they rear up on their hind legs, striking only with their front hooves.

but the view right across the countryside was tremendous. The marsh was bor=
dered by tall trees but my look=out rose above their tops. The swampy terrain
of the wild horses of Dülmen was spread out all around me. Even the Duke of
Croy could never have seen his Merfelder Marsh as well as this.

The herd was widely scattered, family groups grazing close together. From
ground level I could never have seen the groupings as clearly because the perspec=
tive would have confused the distant groups. From above, however, I could see the
individual groups within the herd and the interesting distances between them. In
the family group I could make out the unweaned foal closest to the dam, either
lying down near her or standing close; a little farther away there was the year=
ling and then the two=year=old, sometimes with a foal of her own. Also tagging
along were at the most one or two "aunts". Apart from the unweaned foals it
looked rather like a mothers' meeting with every member waiting for the word
of command from the oldest and the most experienced mare. They all obeyed
the orders of the leading mare. The whole herd of wild horses was a mosaic of
closely knit family parties. It would be quite wrong to assume that the herd was
just a group of random individuals. The significant structure of the herd became
clearer the longer I remained, quietly watching.

The wind was easterly and the herd grazed facing westwards. As gusts of wind
blew across the plain, long wispy tails flattened under the horses' bellies. The whole
scene was one of harmonious uniformity. Then, one of the older mares put her
head up and started to move off with her foal in the direction of a drinking place.
Seconds later the other members of the family were on the move, heading in the
same direction. It was as though the old mare had set the fashion. The others
followed her in single file and soon the whole family party had detached itself
from the grazing herd. Leaving a narrow track of hoof=marks one behind the
other, they trotted along in single file in strict order according to their position
in the social hierarchy. The old mare led the way to the drinking place just as
she did when they were changing pastures or fleeing from some danger which
threatened. The herd lives in this way, maintaining its family communities,
throughout the greater part of the year, for nine months in fact. Then during
the first week in June, year after year, the stallion starts his reign. He endeavours
to subdue all the individual mares with leading roles so that the whole herd will
respond to his command. This hardly ever happens because the family parties
obstinately continue to detach themselves. It is only when extreme danger threat=
ens the whole herd that the leading mares cease to assert their wills against the
stallion.

Wild horses drinking on the Merfelder Marsh. The breed is restricted to this reserve in Westphalia.

From my lofty observation post I also had a view right across the hunting ground. The district forester, Düssel, who was responsible for the whole area, told me that this chase covered 500 acres. It presented a very varied picture, consisting of high forest and coppice, in part regularly thinned, but also some untended forest, scrub, bog, moor and pasture.

From time immemorial the marshes of Westphalia have provided ideal condi= tions for game, and since man set about making the horse useful to him the marshes have been a refuge for wild horses.

I noticed that the gusty weather was constantly driving the herd westwards. Also Klaus Zeeb wanted the horses to be exercising in front of him with the wind against him — or at the very least from the side — so that they would not get his scent too soon as he approached on all fours. It was therefore essential that we should shift our position and, of course, the "Giraffe". I pressed two switches, threw two levers and with a low hiss I was back on the ground again. We soon found a new position and were ready to go ahead. I heaved myself up on to the crow's=nest platform and rose into the air. The early morning squalls appeared to have been suddenly left behind, the wind was steadier and veering; it now blew from the south, making conditions ideal for our experiment.

Down below I watched the young research worker making his way towards the herd, using a drainage ditch as cover. He wanted to reach a sandy hollow in the ground without being seen by the herd and from thence to approach them on all fours. He succeeded in getting into position, but as he stuck his head up to see if the horses were still there two old mares noticed him and warned their family parties. All the animals in these groups looked round cautiously, very much on the alert as the scent of man reached them from the squatting figure of Klaus Zeeb some distance away. I had an excellent view from my crow's=nest and I wished that I had the use of a "Giraffe" for all my animal observations. I looked right over the whole herd and I could detect individual movements within the herd communities, the details of which would undoubtedly have been lost to me if I had been on the ground. From my high angle I could see at a glance that it was a family party in the centre and another one over to the right of me which were the first to be on the alert as Klaus Zeeb showed his head above the grass. All the others continued to graze, showing no sign of unrest, and at this stage even the stallion had not noticed the man.

We know, of course, that some herd animals set a watch — virtually placing an animal on sentry duty — so that the herds shall not be taken by surprise when grazing. In Norway, for instance, on the Dovrefjell, I have actually photographed the female on watch as she stood on guard at the edge of a herd comprising almost a thousand head of wild reindeer. Would Dülmen horses adopt the same instinc= tive behaviour when grazing? The photographs which I took of the horses before Zeeb started the real part of his experiment appeared to support this: the horses with their heads up, watching every movement which Zeeb made, were standing farther away from him than a large number of others which apparently refused to be diverted from their grazing. And yet I am sure these horses had also noticed the man. Why then, in contrast to the other family groups, did they not allow themselves to be disturbed by Zeeb's presence? I would suggest the following explanation: there was no need for them to break off feeding prematurely because others on whom they could rely were on the alert.

A wild animal must continually endeavour to avoid enemies and it spends the greater part of life in flight. In order to maintain its strength, therefore, the horse must be able to feed until the last possible moment before taking flight and life in a herd thus offers good security. Unlike soldiers, whose guard duties are allocated to them, animals from different family parties do not take it in turn to go on watch. The sentry is not appointed by the other animals, it goes on watch of its own accord; it continues as long as its senses are alert and strength permits. It is the old experienced mares who are the sentries on the Merfelder Marsh.

Suddenly the peacefulness of the scene was broken by an angry snort which was clearly audible even at my height from the ground. From a prone position Zeeb had raised himself onto all fours and only "walked" a few yards when the warning was given. At once the first line of grazing horses ran off and those behind watched carefully. Curiously enough it was the family groups farthest away from Zeeb — those grazing far behind the group from which the warning had come — who were the first to withdraw. They did not hurry: they walked away, vacating the area as though they wanted to leave room for the others in front just in case they had to take flight suddenly.

The scientist paused at the edge of the hollow and adopted a characteristic four-footed posture broadside on to the herd, making himself into a typical quadruped. There was an immediate reaction, everything seemed to be on the move except for the mares in the central group which were on watch. They stood their ground but never took their eyes off the quadruped. Then I suddenly caught sight of the stallion standing with his head up, mane and tail streaming in the wind, looking like a statue — mousy-grey in colour with a clearly defined black stripe running the length of his back. He stood on his own, not very far from the four sentries which were giving warning snorts. It looked as though his moment had come, the level of alarm was high enough for the herd to watch for his signals. The man moved forward again, the stallion neighed shrilly and drove the herd away from the danger, keeping them on the move by threatening bites, warning snorts and by charging against them in quick rushes. Even the four old mares, the sentries, yielded immediately and followed on behind the others, bringing up the rear.

The experiment continued with Zeeb still on all fours. Whenever he stopped moving, the horses also stopped and stood quite still, but as soon as he moved forward again the horses fled. In this fashion Zeeb was able to drive the herd of some 200 animals in any direction that he chose. He covered hundreds of yards on all fours, driving the herd farther and farther to the west. It made a grotesque picture: a surging mass of splendid horses fleeing from something small that crawled. The dangerous creature was never allowed to come nearer than six horses' lengths away but when it stood up the horses recognized it immediately as a man. Standing upright, Zeeb could approach the stallion without any trouble, and he stood, still snorting, in front of his herd, allowing himself to be stroked. But the moment Zeeb returned to the quadruped posture the herd scattered, neighing as they fled.

The horses never recognized the human on all fours even when the change from standing to crawling took place as they looked on. Although the human scent remained the same, this made no impression because the horses were more impressed by what they saw. In fact the horses behaved exactly like the chimpanzees in the King Kong experiment when they failed to recognize the human under the ape mask even when the transformation took place before their very eyes.

Animals do not in general have this kind of insight. If they had it, what purpose would it serve? It is quite sufficient for the continued existence of wild horses that, when faced with a quadruped of approximately bear size, they should sense danger and immediately take the appropriate action. Indeed, I would go farther than this and suggest that this lack of discernment is a distinct advantage. If the horses' instinctive reaction to danger were not simple and precise, they would have to pause in order to analyse the cause of their sensation of fear. Instead of the instant visual recognition of potential danger, flight would be delayed and valuable time would be lost which might endanger the herd. The immediate visual stimulus results in a clear sequence of events: four=footed animals of predator size — danger — flight.

It is not surprising, therefore, that when Klaus Zeeb stood upright the Dülmen horses treated him as a man, since in their experience man has always walked on two legs. Nor is it surprising that they regarded the man as having become a "bear" as soon as he went on all fours. It would indeed have been surprising had they behaved in any other way. However, there was one aspect of the results obtained by Klaus Zeeb which astonished me, and this was the fact that all the horses tested by the scientist gave such a clear reaction. I was surprised that the fear of predators is so deeply ingrained that horses in this day and age still react so decisively to a primitive form of danger.

One cannot help asking what purpose can be served by a doctor of veterinary medicine spending his time crawling about a marsh on all fours. Nobody but Klaus Zeeb can give the answer to this:

It is one of the basic tenets of human medicine that all illness is not due solely to physical causes but that some may well be emotional in origin. For a long time this fact received little attention from the veterinary profession. This was undoubtedly due to the difficulty of dissociating animal psychology from an anthropomorphic outlook. The study of behaviour as a whole has recently proved of value in the analysis of animal behaviour in particular. As a result of intensive observations on animals, facts about behaviour are collected and be= haviour patterns are analysed. Knowledge about the ways in which animals react to their environment enables us to provide the best possible living condi=

tions for those in our care. When an animal's behaviour diverges from the nor=
mal, we know that it is living under unfavourable conditions. If it is returned
to a normal environment, it will once again behave normally. The behaviour
of domesticated animals is particularly difficult to analyse. As a result of the
process of domestication and of close contact with man, these animals have
long since diverged from normal behaviour. By observing the behaviour of pri=
mitive races of the corresponding wild form, it is possible to establish original
behaviour patterns where the animals have been virtually free of contact with
man. Remarkably valuable knowledge about horses has been gained by such
methods. Pure behaviour research is fully justified when it leads to practical
results.

Not long ago a well=known expert said: "He who understands the psychology
of cattle is in the best position to promote their health, fertility, productivity and
longevity." Since cattle are our main source of food supply, pure research into
their behaviour is obviously closely linked to our daily lives. The high sterility
rate in herds of domestic cattle is an example of how closely our daily lives — in
fact our daily meals — are linked with comprehensive behaviour studies. The
problem of sterility is not so much one of the physical condition of the animals,
it is almost exclusively a psychological problem. The Veterinary Institute of Frei=
burg University has been studying this subject for years; the special aim of the
group of scientists, of which Dr Klaus Zeeb is a member, is to investigate the be=
haviour patterns of cattle. Cattle, of course, are our main source of supply of meat
and there are misgivings as to whether artificial insemination — practised on one
third of all cows in the West German Republic — is not the cause of increasing
sterility in agricultural herds. As a result of their research, the investigators at
Freiburg are decisively in favour of a return to natural mating in order to coun=
teract this alarming trend.

CHAPTER 6

The Fight of the Stallions

IT WAS BEAUTIFUL spring weather when I was invited to pay a visit to the Arab stud farm at Achental, which lies four miles south of the well-known beauty spot of Chiemsee. The green meadows at the foot of the Upper Bavarian Alps were very inviting and I spent the morning lying amongst the foals in the grass.

The stallion, Vishnu, was bridled and exercised for my benefit. Circling on the lunging rein he looked like a fiery comet and it seemed to me that he was well named. For Vishnu is the name of one of the illustrious triumvirate of Hindu gods, and it is said that at one time his soul dwelt in a horse before achieving its highest state. The stallion came from Poland, from a whole line of Arabs descended from the famous stud of Janow-Podlasky. When the war came the most valuable bloodstock was moved to Germany. But the fortunes of war were such that the stallion found himself a member of a travelling circus.

At Achental I learnt quite a lot about Vishnu. He was blind in the left eye through an injury said to have been caused by a badly aimed lash of the whip in the circus ring. He proved unsuitable for circus work and a farmer from Holstein bought him for work on the land. There, quite by chance, the horse was seen by Traude Griesbach, the owner of the Grassau stud, who noticed his outstanding quality. She recognized the hereditary factors which gave him his fiery temperament and noble bearing and she decided that he was well worth putting to stud. The farmer agreed to part with him and so the Arab from Poland became Lord of Achental.

The mares running with the stallion from Poland were descended from Babolna of the Arab stud in Hungary, others came from the royal stud of Württemberg, and so the progeny were indeed of noble descent. A new Arab population had been growing up at Achental with Vishnu as its sole overlord and over the years his progeny filled the paddocks. It was considered far too risky to allow any other stallion to meet him. As soon as the colts were over two years old they began to show some interest in the mares. As leader of the herd Vishnu immediately regarded them as potential rivals and he was not slow to challenge them. If Vishnu met one of these half-grown youngsters in the same paddock he would attack mercilessly and beat the life out of him. The struggle for supremacy is in the blood of every stallion whatever its race and Vishnu was no worse tempered in this respect than any other. It is true that these natural drives have been suppressed through a thousand years of domestication and living closely with man. But, given a few days of wandering freely in the herd, it is surprising how vigorously the habits of wild forebears reassert themselves.

Besides Vishnu I saw two of his male offspring, Kaid and Raschid and the other likely males. There is virtually no problem of succession in a wild herd where all the horses run freely together. Rivalry is dealt with as it emerges and the solution is found in savage combat. Such contests nearly always result either in the death of one of the contestants or in serious injuries. Naturally no stud can afford to solve its problems of succession in this way since losses are inevitable. Stud farms are very costly to run and scarred animals cannot be sold.

Kaid and Raschid were both considered to be likely successors to Vishnu and it was clear that neither would be for sale. In view of this I wondered if there would be any chance of watching a combat between them. Fights between stallions are rarely seen and I was anxious to see one in all its various phases. I was particu= larly interested in observing the ritual behaviour in the early stages of the contest. I discussed the possibility of allowing the two stallions to meet and asked the management whether it would be possible to organise some method of separating the two animals before the final climax. It was obvious that whatever happened one stallion must not be allowed to gain full victory over the other. The manage= ment raised no objections, and it was agreed that the two animals should be allowed to meet in a certain paddock with the staff, suitably armed with crops and whips, standing by on all sides.

A paddock surrounded by a very high fence was selected for the arena to pre= clude the possibility of either horse's jumping out and gaining its freedom when in a highly excitable state. The choice of meeting place was therefore to some extent forced upon the stallions and, had they been free to choose their own site for the start of the fight, they might well have selected one which was less restricting. The space was somewhat limited and, with no room for flight, there was not much opportunity for the stallions to take evasive action and it was a case of having to stand up to each other. I hoped that these conditions which were imposed on the animals would not distract their attention, and the stud grooms shared my hopes that the natural vigour of the stallions would make them blind to every= thing but each other.

We need not have worried. There was a reaction from Raschid as soon as Kaid was let out of his box. Raschid was the first to enter the paddock and he scented his rival from a distance. As Kaid was led in the direction of the paddock, Raschid trotted over to the gate, pawed the ground, and effectively blocked the way. We had not expected this. Kaid was equally well aware of Raschid and he showed temper with his groom, struggling to get free from control and meet Raschid with the least possible delay. Had we opened the gate the two horses would have run everyone down and so, right at the start of the encounter, we were forced to intervene. Two men drove Raschid back from the gate, shouting and cracking their whips so that eventually he reluctantly gave ground and withdrew to the far corner.

The gate was opened quickly and quietly, Kaid needed no persuasion to enter, the poles were slipped into place and the two stallions were shut in. Having seen their first reaction while still a considerable distance apart, I assumed that now that there was no barrier between them they would make a savage rush at each other without standing on ceremony. This, however, did not happen. On the con= trary, it seemed as though their proximity came as something of a shock and they sobered down immediately. Each behaved as though he did not see the other. Kaid appeared to be in no hurry and Raschid, with his flank exposed to Kaid, started to graze. Both appeared outwardly to be remarkably calm but I could see their muscles working and every fibre strained to the limit under the skin. Kaid stood stock=still, snorting provocatively now and again through distended nostrils. Raschid went on grazing quietly. Suddenly Kaid's tail arched. It shot up vertically as though released by a spring, forming a right angle with his back, leaving the long tail hairs streaming in the breeze. Raschid still did not look up but continued to graze, slowly but surely increasing the distance between himself and Kaid. Was he shirking the contest, would there be no fight after all? On the other hand, everything that happened in the arena appeared to be deliberate, as though it had some purpose. As a spectator I felt as though I were witnessing the preliminary rituals in a duelling code. In the meantime Raschid had walked into a position where his head and body were almost in line ahead of Kaid. The stallion's grazing was apparent only. There was no grass in this particular enclosure and so he could not actually feed. He went through all the motions, however, and his movements were precisely those of grazing. This was a pure displacement activity, similar to that of a human being who rubs his chin or scratches his head when he is not sure what to do next.

Kaid appeared to wait while Raschid reached this position. Then he neighed loudly and turned himself right round, stamping his hooves alternately hard on the ground, until he had his back to his opponent. With their haunches facing, both looked out in opposite directions, addressing each other sharply with their tails. Then both animals evacuated, almost simultaneously. Was this due to the extreme nervous tension? It would be perfectly natural, as it occurs in other mam= mals — including man — in similar situations. On the other hand it could have had some other significance.

Both Arabs were almost bursting with pent=up energy. Snorting, they pawed the ground with their front hooves as though trying to dig a hole. Kaid put his head up and neighed challengingly; seconds later Raschid replied. Both were still facing in opposite directions but they could just see each other, because it only needed a minute movement of the head to one side for the opponent to be in view. The visual angle of a horse's eye is like an ultra wide=angle camera lens; with each eye the horse is able to cover an arc of about 160° and with the use of both eyes only a tiny part of the circle is out of vision. Thus even when standing rump to rump each could see his rival excellently.

They remained in this position for only a few seconds. Suddenly Kaid roared and stood up on his hind legs, adopting a typical heraldic pose, displaying the tremendous muscular power of his hindquarters. He listened, with his ears laid back, for any reaction to his challenge. Raschid's answer to this flamboyantly aggressive posture was to paw the ground and pretend to graze. Kaid re=issued the immensely provocative challenge. For one brief moment Raschid presented an open flank towards his opponent but he turned away again abruptly and, pawing the ground and grazing, he shuffled backwards towards Kaid. The latter did the same except that he did not graze. His front hooves pounded the ground while his hind legs trembled, tense and ready to strike.

This was the last detail which I was able to absorb. Two brown streaks of light= ning flashed out at each other as the stallions let fly. Hooves thudded dully against bellies, dirt flew in all directions and the stallions screamed as they circled round each other furiously. Each tried to strike the other on the flank or to bite the withers and the back. They went round and round, foam flying as they snorted, exchanging blows and bites, spinning along the length of the tall fence. This was an out=and=out fight with no holds barred. The horses crashed together and blows found their marks. The shutter of my camera clicked furiously but I could no longer distinguish between the stallions in the general mêlée. So far neither of them appeared to have gained dominance over the other. Both had drawn blood.

Throughout the battle the men stood all along the edge of the paddock holding whips and staves, waiting for the right moment to intervene. Suddenly the stal= lions pirouetted into the air, balancing on their hind legs as they struck out with their forelegs. The eyes of both horses were squinting with the shortness of the distance between them and the narrowness of the angle of vision. I managed to recognize Raschid with his back to me, neighing and screaming, fighting like a maniac. Kaid had succeeded in ripping the skin off his rump and this bite had apparently driven Raschid mad; he struck out furiously with his forelegs, landing hard connecting blows with his hooves. In this way he succeeded in driving Kaid into a corner, and it looked as though Kaid's situation was getting desperate be= cause he could no longer escape to the rear. Raschid whipped round to the left and pranced in to the attack. All at once Kaid dropped down on to all four legs. Raschid immediately followed suit, turning his back ready to lash out with his hind hooves. But Kaid trotted away. He had had enough, for one round at least. Raschid neighed triumphantly and raised his long tail vertically into the air. Was the victor hoisting the flag?

It was too soon to claim victory. Kaid trotted back to the place where the fight had started and again took up position, making a show of posturing, neighing and snorting. I noticed that his hind feet were standing on the spot where he had previously defaecated. Whilst Kaid made a show of starting the ritual afresh, Raschid left his corner and walked quietly to take up his position. He returned to the place where the fight had started for him and in so doing his hind feet also touched his own excrement. It crossed my mind that "marking" with a pile of dung might be part of the ritual of a stallion fight but I had no time to reflect on this because the second round of the fight was under way with the horses circling and frequently rearing up on their hind legs and screaming. Again and again they tried to bite and get a grip on their opponent. Then Kaid fell. I never saw how it happened but immediately Raschid's teeth sank into Kaid's neck. There was no more photography; something hit me in the side as the men rushed in from all sides to separate the stallions. It was not a moment too soon. I stumbled but ran with them. The victor was driven back with whips and the two stallions were kept apart by the staves as Kaid got to his feet. Blood was running down his neck from a broad laceration which fortunately was not deep. But Kaid would have been trampled to death by Raschid if the men had not rushed in.

We walked back to the stables and I looked at the rival stallions in their boxes. Their wounds were not severe but it was a sobering thought that one crack of those hooves on a human skull would send us flying from this world to the next.

CHAPTER 7

Maxi – the Condemned Squab

DR JÜRGEN NICOLAI stood on the balcony of his house in the afternoon sun=shine, looking towards the shores of the lake. He was searching for something in the tops of the birch trees which frame the lake at Seewiesen. He glanced at his wrist=watch as he turned to speak to me: "It's three o'clock, he ought to be here by now because he knows that this is the time when we usually meet. He's a most interesting chap, you must meet him." And, laughing, he added, "He's parti=cularly attached to me." Dr Nicolai is an Assistant at the Max Planck Institute for Behaviour Physiology at Seewiesen near Munich. He is a colleague of Professor Konrad Lorenz, and the chap he had just recommended to me as worth meeting was a domestic pigeon of male sex – a pigeon called Maxi with a rather unusual history.

To all outward appearances Maxi was a perfectly ordinary domestic pigeon, well=built and in good condition, but he was different from all the other members of his species at Seewiesen – he was English. Maxi came from the heart of the City of London, from a niche in the wall of an old Victorian building not far from Fleet Street. He was condemned to death before he had even hatched. Pigeons were increasing so fast that their numbers were to be reduced. Maxi had already begun to chip his way out of the egg=shell when the nest was completely walled in. His parents escaped but it looked as though Maxi's chalky prison would end up as his coffin. Fortunately for Maxi he was imprisoned within reach of a window and his plaintive cheepings were heard by a lady who was fond of birds. She leant out of the window and broke the brick out of the fresh mortar. She knew how to rear young pigeons and she took the blind nestling and fed him with some special soft food from her mouth. This may sound a difficult operation but it is an inborn reaction in young pigeons to stick their beaks into cracks and crevices immediately after hatching; in this way they inevitably find their parent's gape after a short time; the parent bird, stimulated by the touch of the squab's bill, regurgitates the food from its crop and the tiny nestling receives the food.

The first few hours and days were critical but Maxi got through them safely and it seemed as though everything could proceed normally. His troubles, however, were not over. His foster=mother suddenly had to take an urgent trip to Germany. Maxi was still at the stage when feeding from the mouth was essential to his survival. There was only one thing to do, and the kind lady took the little Cockney pigeon with her. He might not need a passport or an air ticket but he still had to be fed every two hours at least. Feeding a pigeon on an aeroplane and in hotels was very difficult, and the good lady found she had saddled herself with a major problem which was interfering with her plans. She wondered how she could pos= sibly find him a home where someone would be prepared to feed him from the mouth for almost three more weeks. But Maxi was born under a lucky star. By chance the Englishwoman was given the address of the research scientist at See= wiesen, and this was how Dr Nicolai assumed the role of foster=father to Maxi, feeding him by mouth as part of his parental duty.

It was Dr Nicolai who named him Maxi when, much later, he found the young pigeon was a male. Squabs do not open their eyes until four or five days after hatching. Maxi saw the light of day for the first time almost immediately after his arrival at Seewiesen. It seemed that the feeding by mouth formed a strong bond between the two creatures of different species. Maxi was imprinted on Dr Nicolai, that is, after a brief period of learning when young, Maxi had formed an attachment to a human instead of to another pigeon. His human father was everything to him and for the first few weeks and months after he was fledged he took no interest in other pigeons.

Maxi thrived and when fully fledged he went out with his foster=father, flying free and keeping him company. Best of all he liked to amuse himself with Dr Nicolai's hand. He played and flirted with it, now parading in front of it as though to make an impression and then displaying to it, behaving as though the human hand were his intended wife. He was also often at the scientist's feet. A man's head and shoulders became Maxi's favourite landing=places — but only those of his foster= father Jürgen Nicolai.

I waited on the balcony, standing well behind Dr Nicolai so that if Maxi should arrive I would have a chance to photograph the greeting or anything that might happen. We did not have long to wait. The foster=father called towards the foliage of the trees and a grey pigeon flew swiftly in a straight line towards us out of the birches; with an elegant dash he landed purposefully on the scientist's head, took one or two pompous steps in his hair and had a good look around. Then he caught sight of me. I was standing quite close to Dr Nicolai because I wanted to take some big close=up photographs of him on his master's head. This appeared to offend the pigeon and before I had time to take a picture Maxi took off, pulling out some of his master's hair in the process; he landed on my left shoulder and at once started to attack me. He beat at my throat with his wings, pecked and nipped the lobe of my ear and then went on beating me with his wings. It was not particularly painful but I certainly noticed it. Dr Nicolai grabbed Maxi and placed him on the broad balustrade of the balcony and I stepped back, somewhat dis= comfited by the unexpectedness of the attack. I wondered if Maxi interpreted my proximity to Dr Nicolai as an attack on his beloved master or whether the pigeon saw me as a rival wishing to court his paramour.

My cautious withdrawal appeared to satisfy the pigeon, which began to show a close interest in the zoologist's hand, probing the dark clefts between the fingers with his beak — he was searching for food, which he always found on this man. He then started to flirt in earnest with the human hand, walking all around it and cooing, as though courting a female pigeon. I took a number of pictures of this remarkable example of an animal imprinted on a human. Then a snow=white pigeon appeared in my viewfinder. She had already settled briefly on the balus= trade once before while Maxi had been attacking me. Dr Nicolai called out ex= citedly: "This should be good, watch what happens. She is one of my female pigeons and Maxi has to decide which he loves more: me and my hand or the white female." The white pigeon looked inquisitively, possibly even jealously, but certainly with attentiveness as Maxi continued to address the human hand. Then she turned away, as though having lost all interest, and started the age=old ritual of head turning. Had I been on my own I would have assumed that in this ritual she was merely preening herself but Dr Nicolai knew his pigeons. He re= cognized their typical movements and understood their meaning. He knew, for instance, what it meant when the white pigeon aimed her beak at certain parts of her plumage and he was able to interpret the language of pigeon preening to me.

When a female preens ostentatiously in front of a male pigeon — just as the white one was doing — this has nothing to do with keeping the feathers clean. The preening movements have a ritual significance and follow a recognizable pat= tern. Step by step the ritual is followed, each action being correctly emphasized and deliberately made. She uses these preening motions as an outward demons= tration of her feelings; with her voice she proclaims that she is attracted to the male.

Our white pigeon started her ritual preening by resting her chin on her breast. She then drew her neck feathers, one by one, between her mandibles. As she did this her hackles rose, revealing the skin between the feathers. This represented an invitation to the male of her choice: "Please nibble my neck or head, I trust you implicitly." It is worth mentioning, in passing, that when other species erect their hackles this may have a totally different significance — in buntings, for instance, it is an indication of alarm.

The submissive preening went on for several minutes but it represented an introduction only. It was not long before the snow=white pigeon turned her head completely round so that it faced backwards, her bill pointing to the middle of her back, aiming at first immediately between the wings. After she had put her bill right into the feathers on her back, she raised her head for a fraction of a second, repeatedly glancing quickly in Maxi's direction. With each renewed burrowing of her head into the plumage on her back, the action of cleaning in= clined more to the left wing. All her movements were precise and rhythmical, directed at making the male aware of her: "Look at me, look at me!"

Maxi behaved as though he did not see the female and continued to caress the human hand. She suddenly stopped in the middle of preening, took two or three formal steps towards him, fixed him firmly with her eyes, dropped her wings and fanned her tail, meaning: "You are so attractive." Maxi still did not react. But there was no need for the white female to be down=hearted for she still held the trump card — in her primary feathers. She raised her wings high and searched her left wing with her bill, going deeper and deeper. She kept on turning her head pur= posefully until finally it disappeared between her wings over her back, leaving her hackles raised invitingly. Her head quivered as she preened, hidden from view. Blind with sexual excitement she preened in a particular spot between her pri= maries and secondaries. Every male pigeon is driven frantic by this movement and Maxi was no exception. He hopped off the human hand and attacked it violently. Where previously he had caressed, he now pecked sharply, making Dr Nicolai cry out.

The white pigeon had won. With her wing play she had expressed her com= plete devotion to the male. While Maxi attacked the "rival male", she watched with great interest but she knew he would soon turn to her and she was confident of the outcome. She was, of course, quite right. He soon strutted in front of her, cooing and crooning, with eyes only for the white female, not even glancing at the human. She flew up into the air, spreading her wings to their full span above Maxi. The light shone through her feathers, revealing the perfect structure of her wings, as she hung jubilantly in the air before dropping down close to Maxi. Inflated with pride, he resumed his strutting and parading before her.

Then she flew away, drawing him after her. At least, that is what it looked like, but she was not leading him, although she was in front. He was driving her ahead of him. He had no home ready but he was driving her away from a rival mate and would later drive her into a nesting hole so that he could protect her more easily from the attentions of other males. During the mating season pigeons behave with exaggerated affection but if the female goes anywhere near another male she is ruthlessly belaboured by her mate. He beats her with his wings and feathers fly in the nesting hole. This does not prevent him from paying court to her for all the world to see five minutes later — in fact, far from preventing him, it appears to incite him. The female submits to it all. Both she and her mate are descended from rock doves which breed in holes in cliffs, and generations of female pigeons have submitted to being driven into a nesting hole. Our white female was no exception.

When an excited male struts in front of a female with his primaries spread and his tail depressed and turns on his axis uttering soft cooing notes, the female is obliged to start her further play ritual, which leads to the male's turning his head. Everything that follows stems from the stimulus which she gives him by this movement; but why the female, at the peak of their excitement, should preen precisely between the last primary and the first secondary feather of her wing remains a mystery.

Dr Nicolai and I left the balcony and stepped back into the room as the pigeons disappeared from view. I started to pack up my photographic equipment while Dr

Nicolai explained to me how Maxi knew the whole house in detail. As a cliff=breeder, he had an innate weakness for dark holes. On one occasion he had an=nexed a dark corner of the kitchen cupboard and had begun to clear it out ready for settling down there when the lady of the house, rather naturally, drove him out. On another occasion he fancied an open cupboard containing books but he was ejected before he got a firm foothold. After this he chose the top shelf of a toy cupboard in the nursery. Dr Nicolai's daughter, Marion, was three years old when this happened and the pigeon would have been quite happy to nest there. The older Maxi grew the more he appropriated the house. This undoubtedly advanced the cause of scientific investigation into pigeon behaviour but the scientist's wife had a rather different point of view. She longed for the day when the orphaned pigeon would fall in love with a real pigeon out in the woods so that her house could cease to be a dovecote.

There was a shout from Marion's room: "Papa, Papa! Come quickly, Maxi is back again." I got my equipment out again and quickly assembled the electronic flash. Sure enough, the pigeon had entered through the door which opened onto the balcony and was standing in the toy cupboard, making deep bows, fanning his tail and inflating his crop. Deep, monosyllabic cooing notes came from the cupboard, a nest=enticing call. He waxed thus for minutes at a time. I made to move nearer with my camera, but Dr Nicolai warned me to keep back, in case the white female should respond to the calls and come into the room. A white blur appeared and she hopped onto the doorstep, waiting to make sure it was safe to enter. I watched her through my viewfinder, she was coming closer and I could hear her claws tapping as she walked on the linoleum. Maxi's cooing continued, enticing her towards this beautiful nestinghole. She flew up and settled for a moment on the arm of a chair from which she could view the hole from a distance. The male pigeon renewed his coaxing, calling still more urgently. The deep, vibrating notes were fascinating even to the human ear. The female raised her left wing and, with a deliberate gesture, she preened the exciting spot, confirming that she approved of the home and was ready. Then she flew by the cupboard, passing quite close to it for a detailed inspection, continued right round the room and returned to land right in the nestinghole, which Maxi had vacated as she flew round the room. Domestic pigeons accept the presence of humans as a matter of course, they are not shy and will carry out the whole ceremony of their ritual quite uninhibited by our presence. Young Marion was delighted by this addition to the collection of things which littered her room. Maxi displayed above his new home, turning in circles, interested only in his snow=white mate. With exaggerated formality he strutted and cooed: "Here sits my wife, all this belongs to me!"

Dr Nicolai approached Maxi very cautiously, holding out his hand to him, but Maxi was prepared to risk everything in defence of his property and he at once went in to the attack. He trod on the hand with splayed toes, beating his wings, pecking and biting the fingers. He tried with all his strength to drag the hand away, continually beating it with one of his wings, while the other was held at a high angle, like a sail, making Maxi look larger than life. He fought savagely. Nothing remained of his previous affection for the human; his foster=father was now only seen as a rival who had made an approach to the female. Dr Nicolai must, therefore, be driven off completely as quickly as possible from the vicinity of the hole.

Once the female has accepted the invitation and moved in, a magic circle sur= rounds the dwelling of the pigeon pair and this gives the male the blind courage to attack everything which shows signs of invading his territory. In this instance Maxi would have succeeded in driving the human hand over the invisible boundary of his territory if the polished surface of the wood had not been so slippery. Any wild pigeon would have given ground before such a furious attack.

Gentle as a dove? After meeting Maxi I was not so sure that I agreed with this simile.

When a female dove preens demonstratively in front of a male it has nothing to do with keeping her plumage clean. Ritual preening plays a significant role in arousing the male. The ritual starts with her chin being drawn in on her throat, thereby raising the feathers on her neck while she preens her breast. She then swings her head round and makes a series of movements directed over her back.

◀ Her tail is depressed and her wings raised high while she preens rhythmically in a precise spot between her primaries and secondaries. This arouses intense excitement in the male.

The male dove was busily engaged in billing and cooing with the hand of his human foster=father when a snow=white female dove arrived (above). The seductive female preened so feverishly and in such an exciting manner that she cast a spell over him. At once the human hand lost its original connotation and the male pecked and beat it with his wings (below). Feminine charm had won the day. She watched the male attacking the human hand and then made it quite clear to him that she was by no means indifferent to his attractions.

The white female suddenly launched herself triumphantly into the air and landed right in front of him. Meanwhile the human hand was withdrawn. The male parades before the beautiful female who had declared her unqualified love by placing her bill under her wing. He struts before her with formal steps, cooing and purring from his inflated throat. His pretentious mannerisms are a response to her ritual preening. When she made the feathers stand apart on her neck, she was saying in effect: "I am yours, come and nibble my neck."

The story of the dove with two dads: two pigeons bill and coo in an aviary made safe from predators in the grounds of the Max Planck Institute of Behaviour Physiology. One of them was a Barbary dove and the other a collared turtle dove, both of them wild birds which build their nests in trees. They preen each other's feathers at the throat and round the eyes. It was obvious that these two were very much attracted to each other as they started to build their nest.

The nest was ready for the eggs. After a considerable time had elapsed without the appearance of any eggs, the behaviour scientist came to the conclusion that both of the birds were males. There was every excuse for the human observer and the doves having made such a mistake, because the courtship behaviour of the male and female dove is so similar that even the birds them= selves may be deceived. Dr Nicolai tried an experiment. He put a fertile egg in the nest and watched to see if the doves would accept it. The collared turtle dove was the first to notice the egg. He looked at it from all angles and naturally assumed that his mate had laid it. He manœuvred it carefully under his breast with his beak and started to brood it. He inflated his throat and cooed as though he would burst in his efforts to make his calls heard.

The other dove heard the calls of his mate on the nest. Assuming that at last an egg had been laid, he gave his best display flight over the fir tree. He then landed on the nest in order to take over the brooding. As doves normally lay two eggs Dr Nicolai smuggled another into the nest. After fifteen days the collared turtle dove put his beak down into the nest and picked up an empty eggshell. He flew off with it and dropped it some distance from the nest, in order that no predator should sus= pect that a young bird had hatched in his nest.

The wonder child looks as though it is covered with dry grass, and those unattractive dark knobs will soon become eyes. In five days' time the chick will be able to see and it will take crop milk from the throat of the adults. The second egg was addled.

CHAPTER 8

A Dove with Two Dads

MAXI WAS ONLY one of many pigeons in which Dr Nicolai was interested. He kept thirty free=flying wild pigeons in the grounds at Seewiesen. He told me many interesting facts about the hatching and rearing of the young and I undertook to make a photographic record of a wild pigeon chick from the time its parents mated to its own fledging. It so happened that the nest which I selected for photography provided a very strange story.

It was in 1962 and I had hoped for an early spring so that the birds would mate and hatch their young without undue delay. Snow, rain and hail kept the tem=perature well below average, however, and it seemed as though spring would never come. Continuous rain was not exactly encouraging and I had a certain sympathy with the birds; it was scarcely the weather for mating. I waited all through March and in April a few pairs of wild pigeons started to build nests. As these pigeons build in trees it was important for me to find a nest which was accessible for photography. To be on the safe side I kept an eye on two pairs who were building at a reasonably convenient height from the ground; one was over six feet and the other only about four and a half feet. Dr Nicolai thought the latter had a poor chance of survival as it was well within the reach of stoats. To make matters worse, losses amongst the free=flying pigeons, due to predation, were higher than usual this spring. There were hundreds of experimental animals in the grounds at the Institute and predators poured in from the surrounding countryside, which was completely wild. Hunting conditions were easy for the predators and they came by day and night. From foxes to weasels and goshawks to tawny owls, they were drawn as if by a magnet to the rich supply of prey. The staff of the Institute were constantly putting out fresh traps, and seldom finding one empty for twenty=four hours. With the exception of the foxes, the trapped animals did not meet an unhappy fate. On the contrary, they could look forward to becoming passengers

Both the male adults rear the youngster and with the double portions the spoiled chick soon has a swollen crop. It will shortly be fledged. The Barbary dove is already thinking about a second brood and offers his mate a present with which to start building a new nest.

in one of the scientists' cars, and they were driven miles before being released once again into the wild.

Dr Nicolai had endless trouble with pigeons both inside the aviaries and out= side, trying to protect them from predators. In this particular spring he had lost a great many outside, taken from the nest at night. Among wild pigeons it is customary for the female to brood at night, the male taking over by day; conse= quently predation at night regularly resulted in the loss of the female from a pair. Owls and pine martens had caused such a decimation of the pigeon population that there was a big surplus of males in this particular year. This fact undoubtedly had something to do with the strange events which took place at the nest which I had selected to watch and photograph.

It was the second half of April before two eggs finally appeared in the highest nest I had selected. The other pair, lower down, were rather amusing because, although their nest looked quite satisfactory to me, they kept on adding to it with tremendous zeal. It was a remarkably solid structure. Although they contin= ually displayed to each other with great ardour, something appeared to be de= laying the actual laying of eggs. Dr Nicolai was of the opinion that it was still too cold for the female. He was particularly interested in any young which might result from the mating of this pair as they would be hybrids. The parents were both collared turtle doves, of different but closely related races: one was the true collared turtle dove which was at one time distributed only from Japan to Turkey, but which has recently spread through the Balkans and Germany as far as Den= mark, Finland and England; the other was a Barbary dove. Dr Nicolai was studying the transmission of hereditary factors and, since the calls of birds are frequently inherited and, with few exceptions, cannot be changed by learning, he was parti= cularly interested in the calls of hybrid chicks. In a mating of the two races, which calls would be transmitted to the offspring? How would the hybrid chicks call and how would their eventual offspring call? Research of this nature can spread over years. Dr Nicolai was understandably concerned about every hybrid egg. Any accident to a clutch could set his research back for years.

One morning towards the end of April Dr Nicolai went to check the nests as usual. He found the higher of my two nests quite empty. The stoat had done its work thoroughly although not where we had feared it would happen. So I was left with the lower nest. This pair still had no eggs but they sat on the wire=netting roof of an aviary, not far from the firtree containing their nest, billing and coo= ing like a pair of proverbial lovebirds. I still could not tell the female apart from the male in this pair, so I asked Dr Nicolai which was which. He rubbed his chin and frowned. He was not sure himself and explained to me why: "Judging from their behaviour in the early stages I would have said that the Barbary dove was the male and the collared turtle dove the female. When the nest was finished, the one I thought was the male sat on the nest and started to brood; this was typical of female behaviour and so I was not sure. Then, suddenly, the collared turtle dove started to sit and brood. . . .''

With pigeons the first egg is normally laid ten days after the first attempt to brood but this nest was still empty, while both of the birds sat and cooed. Four days later there were still no eggs and Dr Nicolai suspected that he knew what was wrong but he gave them another two days and then he was certain: there never would be any eggs because they were both male.

It may seem odd that the pairing of two birds of the same sex should ever take place under natural conditions, but this can be explained quite easily. Both males had lost their mates at a time when the mating drive was at its height; with their mates suddenly gone — taken by predators — they displayed to each other. The sex of pigeons cannot be recognized from external characteristics, and as the be= haviour of the male and female is very similar it does not affect the ritual much if one mistakes the sex of the other. It is true that there were minor discrepancies in the accepted pattern of behaviour but in the desire to gain a partner each male overlooked what he may have regarded as slightly faulty female behaviour. Neither pigeon drove the other away, which is what usually happens when two males come too near each other, and consequently each assumed the other was a female. In this way the association between the two males was formed. The super nest was also due to the fact that the pair consisted of two males. The male nor= mally builds the nest, the female playing only a minor role in this. Had two females built the nest in the firtree it would have been a slovenly affair. The size and solidity of the nest was the result of two males' having taken part and we ought to have realized this earlier. We noticed the fact that the birds seemed to be adding unnecessarily to the nest but it did not enter our heads that there were two males concerned.

The situation was unique. Zoologists had seldom if ever observed a pair of male pigeons building a nest together and even attempting to breed. We knew that each of the males was waiting for the other to lay an egg and naturally nothing would have come of the affair if Dr Nicolai had not intervened. He wondered if perhaps the two males might even incubate and rear the young if he provided them with an egg. And so, on 3 May, he put a fertile, hybrid egg into the nest.

We withdrew and waited tensely for the return of the birds. My camera was already mounted on the tripod, the telephoto lens extending practically into the nest. The egg looked very white in the darkness of the firtree. Would the pigeons see it? Would they accept it? Usually they were somewhere around the firtree but now nobody came. Then I heard a rustle to my right: the Barbary dove had landed on the aviary roof but he went off again immediately. Had he noticed the egg? He came down again, hopped quite quickly along the branches towards the nest and then stared. Another hop nearer and then he put his head on one side looking at the egg from all sides. He walked about a little as though saying: ''I had absolutely nothing to do with it.'' Then he stepped forward carefully, ob= viously accepting the egg, fluffed out his feathers, sat right down over it and began to incubate.

We breathed again, we had achieved it. I had taken photographs at each stage and my back ached. I dared not stop for a breather. The Barbary dove inflated his crop until I thought he would burst: "Guk=gruuuh=guk=Rrruuguk," he called again and again, letting his partner know of the happy event. The collared turtle dove must have heard the call from the firtree because he was suddenly overhead, bursting out of the tree in a spectacular display flight. Loud wing claps announced that he had fully understood the latest news from the nest. Shortly afterwards he was back in the lower branches of the tree carrying some nesting material in his beak. Since the nest was obviously complete one might well ask what was the purpose of this. The answer is that it is part of the male pigeon's ritual: when the first egg is laid his nest=building drive is intensified and he offers the female small twigs; she accepts them and puts them in position without leaving the egg. The two males behaved in an exemplary manner as far as I was concerned, ap= pearing in front of my camera with almost textbook precision and regularity. It so happened that the first pigeon to notice and accept the egg was the Barbary dove and that it was daylight when this happened; the male normally incubates by day and so he naturally took on the day shift. This forced the collared dove — in this abnormal situation — to accept the female role of incubating at night; in fact he arrived in the afternoon to take over the incubation and remained sitting throughout the night. Just as in a normal pair, the two males arrived punctually to relieve each other. The nightshift pigeon was free from about ten o'clock in the morning until three or four in the afternoon. In order to get photographs of the change=over I had to be certain of being there at the right time. They kept to a remarkably accurate timetable, the variation never being more than ten minutes. This division of time between the two birds is as wise as nature herself: it is so arranged that each bird has time to feed in between its periods of duty on the nest. In order to allow the dayshift pigeon enough time to collect food before the onset of darkness, the collared turtle dove arrived sufficiently early in the afternoon and stayed on in the morning. In this way neither of the birds had to sit when cold and hungry.

Pigeons do not lay more than two eggs. The clutch size is as small as this because each parent can only produce sufficient "milk" from its crop to feed one chick; the production of this "milk" by the parents is essential for the successful rearing of the young in the first few days of their life. Our two males, therefore, needed another egg and so Dr Nicolai quickly smuggled them another, which was accepted immediately.

There followed a period of patient waiting. The normal incubation period for pigeons is fifteen days but in order to be quite certain of not missing the hatching of the eggs I took up my position in the firtree two days before they were due to hatch. I might have spared myself the trouble because this pair took precisely fifteen days. In the meantime the birds had become accustomed to my presence. They remained sitting, as though glued to the eggs. They did not seem to mind even when the camera was only twelve inches away from them as they sat.

Around noon of the fifteenth day — strictly according to schedule — there were signs that things were happening. The pigeon on duty became restless: he kept raising himself up and then settling back again, as though trying to let in fresh air under his belly; and he frequently stuck his beak underneath. This went on for quite a time. Suddenly he jerked himself up, his legs wide apart, and appeared to be searching for something with his beak; he pecked and brought out an empty eggshell and immediately flew off with it. I knew that he would drop it at a suitable distance from the nest so that there was no chance that the eggshell might provide any clues for predators as to the location of the nest. I had a quick look into the nest before the pigeon returned. There was a tiny creature lying near the second egg; its head was practically naked and instead of bright eyes there were dull knobs. Pigeons are born blind, it is five days before their eyes open. The beak looked enormous in relation to the whole body; in a newly hatched chick it is so heavy that the head keeps flopping over and this one managed to prop its head on the second egg. After the tremendous effort of trying to get out of the shell, the chick lay exhausted. It was sparsely covered with straw=coloured tufts of down. The chick was no longer wet and I knew from Dr Nicolai that at this particular moment it must be at least one hour old. Apparently the parent bird does not leave the nest to remove the eggshell until the chick is completely dry and this takes one hour. The male was back at the nest in less than a minute. He hopped through the dense branches of the firtree quite close to me as though I did not exist and carefully covered the chick with his body.

The long=awaited event had at last taken place: the two males had produced a child. Would they now succeed in rearing it? One might think that once the chick had arrived it would be less trouble to look after but in fact the contrary is true of pigeons. It is essential that both parents should be ready to produce their "milk" the moment the eggs are hatched and this means that the physiological changes involved in "milk" production must be taking place simultaneously in both birds. They are both concerned with incubating and feeding the chicks as soon as they have hatched. There is no difference in parental duties between male and female in a normal pair and consequently the two males had no particular problems at this stage. They managed to produce their crop "milk" simultaneously so that the chick made good progress. Pigeon "milk" is not liquid but a kind of cheesy broth made up of cells from the inner lining of the crop. It is rich in albumen and gives the young a tremendous start in life.

I was so close that I could see the way in which the parents stimulated the blind chick to look for food. They kept on nudging it carefully with their heads and bills until the young one stuck its beak in every possible crevice. Eventually it found its way between the two mandibles of the parent, which then opened its bill wide so that the chick's beak drove deep into it. With this stimulus the adult regur= gitated the broth from its crop and pressed it into the open beak of the young chick.

Unfortunately there was no sign of life from the second egg and Dr Nicolai removed it. The one chick, reared by the two males, grew remarkably fast. It was offered the same amount of food as was normally available for two chicks and it was scarcely surprising that it was soon so full that it could take no more. The solicitous parents could not understand this. They were forced to get rid of the endless supply of "milk" which they kept producing in their crops. The supply of milk was, in fact, far in excess of demand and I noticed a definite change in the behaviour of the chick and the parents. During the first few days the chick had sat under the adult, begging for food with its wings quivering, as soon as it had learnt how to get its food. Now with its crop full of rich milk, it was completely sated and apparently sick of food. At the start the parents had issued a gentle invitation to the chick to come and feed; this now changed into energetic command. If the chick did not thrust its beak down the adult's throat it was given a thorough drubbing and was cuffed with the adult's wings until it accepted food. And so the chick grew into a young Goliath at lightning speed.

From the sixth day on, when its eyes were open, the chick had a mixed diet of crop milk and pre=digested grain in saliva. Raw grain came a little later. Once again the scientist by my side was able to point out a remarkable piece of beha= viour to me: an adult offering food to a chick can actually decide what food to offer it. It holds in its crop three forms of nourishment: milk, pre=digested food and raw food. The adult knows which of these foods is best for the chick according to the length of its beak. A short small beak stimulates it to give milk. A large long beak stimulates it to regurgitate raw food from the crop.

I visited the nest nearly every day. The only worry I had was that a stoat might suddenly put an end to the idyllic scene. Needless to say, Dr Nicolai was much more nervous than I was. He was naturally concerned for the safety of this remarkable youngster and he would have liked to put the whole nest in an aviary. Every morning he went straight to the firtree before going anywhere else, but in spite of its being built so low everything went well with the nest.

On the eleventh day the juvenile feathers appeared and the chick lost its straw= coloured appearance. These feathers grew so fast that I could almost see them sprouting. Growth needs to be rapid because young pigeons must be fledged by the fourteenth to the sixteenth day. On the thirteenth day Dr Nicolai could not stand the strain any longer and he took the whole lot into protective custody. He simply could not afford to take the chance of exposing this valuable link in his research to the risk of loss by vermin. On the sixteenth day the young pigeon made its first attempt at flight from a firtree surrounded by protective wire=netting. The parent birds did not appear to be unduly upset by Dr Nicolai's intervention. They had already shown signs of renewed courtship and nest=building activities. Some days previously, when they were both still engaged in rearing their young chick, they had indulged in a little flirtation. The Barbary dove was sitting on the nest and, while the quills of the chick were hardening, the collared turtle dove arrived at the nest carrying a present for his mate. His offering consisted of some small twigs, grasses and fine threads. The shared experience of rearing the young chick from the egg seemed to have drawn the two males even closer together. They would soon build another nest and once again they would wait for each other to lay the eggs. This time, however, they would wait in vain and eventually it would dawn on each of them that he had chosen the wrong mate.

The young pigeon flew along the shore of the lake, a self=reliant individual in its own right. No one knew whether this wonder child was a sturdy lad or a charming maiden. Even Dr Nicolai would not know its sex until it had found a mate — and then he would watch to see which one incubated during the day and which by night.

CHAPTER 9

Under an Elephant's Foot

WHEN I STAND in front of elephants I am not averse to having a few strong bars between myself and the animals. I am not ashamed to admit this because there have been occasions in my life when I would have been delighted to find something solid separating myself from an elephant. I am very fond of elephants in spite of this — indeed, perhaps, because of it — and I never lose an opportunity of watching them, whether they are in the zoo, the circus, a nature reserve or in the wild. Often it is not so much what one sees as the circumstances in which one sees it that provide the adventure.

There was a time when I was constantly moving about in the circus world. I knew everybody. I mixed with trainers and animals alike. I was as much at home with the animals in their quarters as I was in the caravans. Trainers often trusted me with their animals and I frequently lived with an act through all its stages, long before it was ready for the ring. In fact the time I liked best of all was either before or after one of the many training sessions, when I could stand in front of the animals in their cages or stalls, alone with them, quietly making my own observations.

All this was some time ago and many of the circus people are now no longer in the ring. Sometimes my old friend William Quindt and I meet together to reminisce about the old days of circus life. It was on one of these occasions, up at his chalet in the Bavarian Alps, that he reminded me of one of my experiences with an elephant called Sandra. I had completely forgotten about it although at the time that it happened it was quite an adventure.

Sandra was one of fourteen elephants in the Swiss Circus Knie. I was on particularly good terms with the trainer, Sepp Hack. He knew my love of being alone with the animals so that I could watch them in peace and he allowed me to go in with them entirely on my own.

Sepp Hack maintained that each one of his elephants was quite definitely an individual with its own particular character. He held the view that recognition of this fact must form the basis of all breaking-in and subsequent training of animals; every animal should be treated as an individual and handled accordingly. It never occurred to me to question his views on training animals because right from the start I was attracted by his methods.

I was very interested in Sepp's relationship with his elephants and the founda=
tions on which it was based. In fact I was so fascinated by his conception of
elephant character that I was determined to try and recapture something of this
with my camera. In order to do this I had first to study my subjects. I had seen
them all in the circus ring and to some extent I knew their special acts. But I
needed to study them individually and I went along to their quarters one lunch=
time so that I could watch undisturbed. Sepp Hack was having a snooze in his
caravan before the afternoon performance. The keeper had already fed and watered
and so I was quite alone with them. In front of me were fourteen grey colossi all
swaying rhythmically from side to side. They were Indian and African elephants
and each one was tethered by the left fore=foot and the right hind=foot, as is custom=
ary with working elephants.

Sepp Hack had impressed on me that no two elephants look alike, each one has
a different head and their characters are as different as their outward appearances.
Unfortunately I had forgotten to ask him what their individual peculiarities were
and it was not until I was confronted with the giants that I realized that a
keeper's dossier on each animal would have been quite useful. The whole fourteen
stood there looking as though they would not even upset a drop of water, in fact
they looked as gentle as lambs. Yet it could be that one of them was not to be
trusted. I had been told their names and the order in which they ranked and I
thought I could remember them. They stood according to their social rating and
according to their compatibility.

Rosa was the first in the row. She was an experienced and extraordinarily
intelligent lady in her middle forties; she could bowl, do sums and carry men
across the arena in her jaws. Although I had already admired Rosa's performance
in the circusring, I must confess that I did not take to her. This was nothing to do
with her character, it was just that when I looked at her she somehow reminded
me of a giant sow. Her head was coarse, her eyes were too small, her movements
were lethargic and altogether she gave the impression of being ponderous and
ungainly. But one should not judge by appearances and inside her bulk there was
a very genuine character coupled with the experience of forty=six years of life.
Rosa's knowledge, her memory and her intelligence were all gigantic. She knew
very well that as the senior member of the circus herd she was entitled to certain
privileges; as well as being first in the ring she was also the first to be fed and
watered. And she was the first to receive a reward after a well=executed act. If any
other animal pushed itself forward Rosa very quickly dealt it a well=aimed blow
with her trunk. All the elephants acknowledged her authority and even the big
tusker, Siam, did as he was told if she so much as cleared her throat. But she never
attempted to use her authority against her trainer. Sepp Hack told me all this
about her later.

The elephant standing next to Rosa, number two in the hierarchy, was called
Sandra, and it was Sandra whom William Quindt had in mind when we chatted
at his chalet. She was considerably younger than Rosa; she looked full of life and

very wide awake, as befitted a young lady of twenty=four. She was also an Indian elephant but she had a much more pronounced profile than her leader and her forehead bulged over rather merry=looking eyes which sometimes had a roguish expression. Her high forehead ended in two lofty domes which gave Sandra a very distinctive outline. I was bewitched by her face. She really was a fascinating creature, I was completely captivated by her expression. I decided to try for a close=up of her face and inevitably I drew nearer and nearer to get the right camera framing; next I concentrated on focussing on the long black eyelashes which emphasized her expressive eyes. Seen like this, her face would make a wonderful elephant portrait and a most unusual study. Suddenly I was no longer in control of the situation. Softly and gently an enormously powerful arm encircled my hips and then drew me irresistibly towards the elephant. There was no chance of resisting. Sandra's trunk had got me. I was in an iron grip, it did not hurt but the pressure was totally unyielding and I knew I could not escape. A thousand thoughts flew through my head: stories about elephants crushing people, dashing them to pieces out of revenge. It was useless to try to think of some way of countering the iron grip—in fact any idea of opposing her was laughable. What could I possibly do? Instinctively I did the right thing, which was not to resist in any way. I took no action at all and let her trunk do exactly what it wanted with me. But I spoke to her repeatedly: "Away, Sandra. Away, Sandra." I had heard Sepp use this phrase. The elephant's eyes were so close to me that I could have counted her eyelashes had it occurred to me to do so. I wondered what was going on inside the enormous head which was right in front of me. Perhaps I was already having hallucinations but it seemed to me that there was mockery, unadulterated mockery, in her eyes. Her trunk pressed me against her side so that the roughness of her hide rasped and scraped. The pressure was quite gentle at first but it grew firmer and firmer. I had a side view of her tongue moving between half=open lips, sliding sensually here and there. I was suddenly terribly hot and sweat poured off me. Sandra must have sensed my fear. Was this the end? An honourable obituary for the deceased animal photographer? Should I shout for help? It was the lunch break and there was not a single keeper about. "Away, Sandra, away," I urged, but her eyes merely mocked me, or so it seemed. I got nearer and nearer to the parted lips and I could see her tongue quite clearly now. Her tongue . . . I suddenly remembered. I had once seen Sepp put his whole arm into Sandra's mouth and scratch the back of her tongue until she grunted with contentment. Perhaps it would work, it was worth trying.

I put my hand carefully into Sandra's mouth and started to tickle her tongue in the middle of its upper surface. It was slippery and pink. She seemed to hesitate, as though taken by surprise, and her eyelids drooped. I ventured farther in, scratching all the time with my fingers, right into her throat. It seemed to me that she winked at me. Suddenly a moan of contentment came rumbling and gurgling from the depths. The uncanny, snake=like grip loosened slightly. The coils of the trunk became wider and the pressure on my kidneys grew less. This was evidently the right approach and I worked away at her tongue assiduously. My arm went right in up to the elbow. The more pleasurable she found it the more she grunted and the wider she wanted to open her jaws. But she also wanted to maintain a firm coil round me. She could not do both and she had to make up her mind: she could either keep a grip on me or she could give herself up to the enjoyment of being scratched. Being truly female she chose pleasure. In order to open her mouth really wide she had to raise her trunk high in the air and the deadly coils started to slacken. Suddenly I was free.

I was released as gently as I had been captured and when I saw her trunk poised above my head like a live question mark, I felt like fleeing. But I could scarcely disappoint Sandra and so I continued to scratch her damp tongue. I thought of making a sudden retreat but I felt that this would be rather a dirty trick. I had the feeling that I ought not to let her think I had cheated her. So I leant against her once again and praised her just as Hack did after she had done a trick well: "Good Sandra, good Sandra." I behaved as though everything was just as it should be and quite normal. After a time I drew out my arm carefully and Sandra did not resist. I looked at my jacket sleeve, it was completely soaked and was not a very attractive sight. I took one step back and Sandra did not object. I fetched a large root of kale from the feeding trough and went up close to her, praising her again and putting the root under her trunk into her mouth. There was a heavy crunch as the kale was crushed between her jaws. Had she wished to do so, she could have done just the same with my arm.

After this alarming half hour we became firm friends. I did not mention the incident to Sepp Hack, I thought it would keep until later, but as it turned out I was able to make use of it much sooner than I had expected. Sandra was due to perform one of her old star tricks in a new programme. The idea was for Sultan, the grey stallion, to gallop into the ring and lie down; Sandra would then walk round him in a circle and finally, to the thunderous applause of the spectators, she would step over him without touching him. Unfortunately it was some time since Sultan and Sandra had performed together and so it was necessary first of all to see if they would still work together. At the first training session, as Sultan was being led up to the elephant, Hack noticed that the stallion was restless and he knew from experience that it would not work. The stallion lashed out with his hind feet and then reared and plunged about so that it was almost impossible to hold him on the long rein. "Take him out," shouted Hack, but Sultan had already broken loose and galloped back into the stable quarters.

The act was already billed in the advance programme. Freddy Knie was not the man to let the public down and he decided that the black horse Othello was the only one who could take Sultan's place. Othello was a magnificent looking horse with a jetblack coat which gleamed like satin. Hack had told me about the failure of the trial with Sultan and so I naturally wanted to see what happened with the black horse. At the first training session nothing that I could photograph occurred; the two animals were not allowed to do anything but walk about together for half an hour. Although this provided no interest for the layman Hack regarded these thirty minutes as of vital importance. The success of the whole training lay ultimately in getting the animals thoroughly familiar with each other. After one week Hack decided that Othello should be allowed to lie down and Sandra should then be led up to him. For safety, all four feet of the black horse were secured and Sacha Houcke, the well-known horse trainer, held his hand over the horse's eye which faced towards the elephant. Fortunately this precaution proved unnecessary: Othello was remarkably phlegmatic. Sandra, on the other hand, held herself as stiff as a board and flatly refused to budge. Nothing would induce her to make a move towards the black body, let alone to step over it. Kind words and titbits had no effect. She was not going to do it and she would not allow herself to be bribed.

Sepp Hack was known to his colleagues as the master of the indirect approach. He showed no impatience but tried another idea: he left the horse lying down and, close beside it, he arranged for a number of men to lie down on top of each other. Without hesitating, the elephant stepped over the human pyramid. Sepp Hack explained to me that he could only use certain keepers for this purpose. It was essential Sandra should know them and like them. "Sandra is a prima donna," he went on, "she is decidedly choosy regarding her partners, whether they're humans or animals. And if something does not suit her it could lead to an accident. A few days ago, just before you went into the elephants' stall, she pulled yet another of the new stable lads towards her and then flung him against a wall. The poor lad is still in hospital with severe fractures. He is the third in four weeks and each of them was given instructions not to go near her."

A shiver went down my spine. There was no doubt that Sandra had intended to do the same with me. Or, at least, this intelligent female had wanted to see how I would behave when she had got hold of me. The elephant test had certainly called for endurance. Sepp, of course, did not know of the secret relationship which I had established with Sandra and I could not resist making capital out of this.

"You know, Sepp, Sandra would walk over me just the same; I don't believe in this business of likes and dislikes," I said provokingly. Hack never liked people to question his statements about his animals.

"Sandra would never step over anyone she did not know, she would rather chuck him on one side. Believe me, I know my animals," he said hotly. "Would you like to bet on it?" I countered, "I am willing to bet she will step over me very carefully and I shall be able to take a photograph of your Sandra from below." I must confess that I did not feel as confident as I sounded but I did not think much could go wrong with Hack standing by.

"It is one way of earning a bottle, Hack," shouted his colleagues encouragingly.

Hack looked at me questioningly: "Are you really serious?"

"Naturally, what do you think?" I replied.

"Right, the bet's on — let's get on with it."

The black horse had already been taken out of the ring. It was my turn now.

My heart was in my mouth. The keepers put down an old sack on the sawdust in the ring. One of my colleagues who happened to be there stood close by, hoping to be able to photograph the trampled remains of Gronefeld!

I walked up to Sandra. Hack's assistant held onto her ear. I came up on the other side so that he could not see me and stuck my hand between Sandra's lips and scratched her tongue gently. A low rumble came from the huge body.

"Quiet, Sandra!" the assistant reassured her, and then, turning to me: "She doesn't like you, you might as well hand over the bottle!"

"Ready?" asked Sepp.

"Ready," I replied and lay down flat on my back. Everything looked different from this angle. Short men looked like giants standing at the edge of the ring. My colleague with the camera grinned. Then a mountain of elephant advanced on me. Her legs looked like enormous grey pillars pounding the ground as they came nearer and nearer. Would Sandra do it? The grey columns loomed larger and larger. I heard Hack's voice, "Lift, Sandra, lift, Sandra." Slowly the right front foot rose; it hung over my stomach. Supposing she put her weight on it? I pressed the camera to my eye. Sand and sawdust dropped on my face. From below, I saw the sole of her foot and where she had trodden on a nail. I had never seen an elephant's foot in such detail before. I remember hoping that no dust would fall on my camera lens. Then, very precisely, Sandra lowered her foot and it came down within a hair's breadth of me — in fact it was so close that it trod on my jacket. This, I suppose, was an elephant's version of made=to=measure. Ten inches farther back and I would have been as flat as a pancake. Then came the left foot. Slow motion, it passed precisely over my face. Once again a rain of dust and the familiar instructions: "Lift, Sandra, lift, Sandra." It was distinctly comforting to hear Sepp's voice and I felt much better than I did on the occasion when I was entirely alone with Sandra and at her mercy. The right hind foot came next and then the left. It was over, she was safely past and I heard Sepp's voice: "Good, Sandra." I jumped up and shook the dust from my clothes. Sepp came over to me: "I don't understand it . . . unless you are the great love of Sandra's life?"

And then I told Sepp of my dangerous adventure with the Indian elephant — the largest girl=friend I shall ever have.

CHAPTER 10

Elephant Dossiers

THE REAL PURPOSE of my observations on elephants was to study their charac=
ters and to document my results by a series of photographs. The alarming inci=
dent with Sandra, although remarkable in its way, was only a by=product of this
work.

There is a connection between the lessons an animal is given and its character.
The training of animals is based on the trainer's knowledge of the individual
animal's personality and it was this link which I wanted to create visually. I
started by studying each one of the fourteen elephants, its position in the herd
and its individual characteristics. It would take too long to describe the dossiers
of all fourteen and so I have selected four. In addition to Rosa and Sandra, there
were two bulls and two cows which I thought worthy of profile treatment. The
Indian bull called Siam was imported from Bangkok when he was already trained,
but before he was purchased Sepp Hack had sent a list of the qualifications which
he regarded as essential for work in the circus ring. He specified: good nature,
high intelligence, quickness to learn and very long tusks. When Siam arrived
there was a note attached to his crate labelled "Instructions for Use". This con=
tained a list of the commands with which he was already familiar.

Elephant bulls in captivity are always unknown quantities and this unpredic=
tability is lurking when the animal is presented to the public in the ring. There
is, therefore, no point in starting a bull in circus work without certain basic quali=
fications. Siam's first duty was to be good=natured and he met this requirement
to the full. He allowed people to do anything to him without showing any sign
of temper or impatience, but he expected the same standard of behaviour from his
trainer. Siam had a very nice sense of what was fair. He was quick to notice any
sign of impatience or harsh words, sensing changes in tone immediately. He would
never have tolerated a lash from the whip. On an order from Sepp Hack, Siam
took strangers onto his tusks with complete equanimity and lifted them high
above his head, carrying them across the circus ring. He did everything willingly
and never got upset by noise and turmoil around him. In the grand finale he took
the place of honour, standing in the centre of a whirling mass of animals, calmly
rotating on his own axis like a spinning top while the animals thundered past
him. Siam's social status was not defined because, although he was the only

Indian male in the herd, he was still young. For this reason Hack allotted him a position slightly apart and he stood six feet to the right of Rosa.

The other male elephant in the herd was an African called Tembo — a Swahili word meaning elephant. He was noticeably more tricky than his colleague from India. It was not that he was ever bad=tempered or that he attacked anyone, but that the African elephant is basically much more difficult to train than the Indian. There are, for instance, no working elephants in Africa. An attempt was made at the end of the last century to train them for work and a school was founded in the Belgian Congo. It remained the only school of its type in Africa and only a few animals were successfully trained and these were sold to zoos and circuses throughout the world.

The African elephant is much more sensitive than the Indian and quickly gets upset if it is not handled properly. Tembo was half sanguine and half choleric in temperament. He was highly intelligent, alert and lively but as sensitive as a mimosa leaf. The usefulness of African elephants in the circus is restricted to some extent by the nature of their physique. Their legs are longer and thinner than the Indian's, which are significantly rounder in cross section, enabling the Indian to stand on its hind legs readily. An African can be made to stand on its hind legs only with difficulty and it tends to become knock=kneed and unhappy. Hack was also not keen on allowing his Africans to do balancing tricks because they are liable to sprains or even dislocations should they slip. Nevertheless they excel at acts involving plenty of movement in the ring. Compared with the stocky Indians, their long lines make them appear quite graceful. They are, of course, decidedly more temperamental but their trunk work is unequalled. An African's trunk is extraordinarily flexible and they can move the distal end on its own whilst holding the remaining part completely motionless. Training of Africans is therefore based on walking and trunk exercises.

Sepp Hack showed me one of Tembo's typical trunk movements: he gave the elephant a piece of cloth to hold between the two "fingers" at the tip of his trunk; Tembo then waved it, moving only the forward end of his trunk. When the Indian went through the same performance, he had to move the whole of his head up and down with the trunk in order to achieve any kind of a wave. The Indian only has one "finger" on the upper side of the trunk tip and can use this as an index=finger to fish things up; the African's two "fingers" are arranged on the upper and lower sides of the trunk tip and they can be used for suction. For instance, they can lift a round object, such as a smooth rubber ball, and carry it around, and they can play musical instruments such as the trombone. For the most part young Tembo was extremely willing and quick to learn but Hack had to be particularly careful not to offend him in any way or he would suddenly turn obstinate and refuse to do anything.

Minjak was a cow elephant from the neighbourhood of Bombay. She was still young and her character was not at all what one might have expected from an Indian. She was high=spirited and exceptionally temperamental; she was also rather irritable and ludicrously ticklish. One day shortly after her arrival from India, her trainer went to rub her back and noticed that she was extremely sensitive to anything which touched her. He could only describe her as ticklish — in fact she enjoyed being tickled so much that she became a perfect fool. Even a sack laid across her back was sufficient to make her go weak at the knees. This gave the trainer one of his many brainwaves. By putting his hands on her back and giving her some food as a reward every time she responded by shaking, he trained her to shake all over on a word of command. He had only to say: "Harder, Minjak, harder," and the young elephant shook so hard that ears, trunk and legs flapped in all directions. This gave rise to a new act called "Minjak the Rock 'n Roller".

Ceylon was introduced to me as the dunce of the party. Not all elephants are intelligent and there are natural simpletons in the elephant world. She was an Indian elephant with a thoroughly phlegmatic approach to life. Nothing worried her, everything was all much the same and things passed her by mainly because she had not got the ability to relate one thing to another. If Hack wanted her to do anything she had to be driven. She was the exact opposite of Minjak, you could whack her really hard on the back without her even moving. Ceylon could only learn things with difficulty and her performance was restricted to acts which she could learn from the other elephants. For instance, she could walk in a circle holding the tail of the elephant in front and she could take part in a pyramid by standing on her hind legs. Hack was unable to use her for anything which required much intelligence but she was useful all the same. If the herd became upset or even enraged, Ceylon would stand peacefully in the middle of the uproar, where she would be as steady as Siam, even if for rather different reasons. She did not mind what was put on her back and the prospect of training her for riding was very good. She had a steady walk and she paid no attention to things which would have driven the other elephants mad. In fact, Hack intended to let a tiger ride on her back when she was a bit older.

All fourteen stood in front of me: Siam, Rosa and Sandra on the right flank, Tembo and Iringa to the left and between them the nine others: Carnauti, Mothi, Ceylon, Minjak and so on. There were as many names as there were personalities. No one animal was like any other. Each one was an individual, requiring a special tone of voice and a way of handling appropriate to its temperament and character. To command this herd, one needed to be a psychologist.

Elephants speak with trunk and ears. Touching the temporal gland with the trunk indicates questioning.

In the Kronberg Reserve for Animal Research, Vauka, an African bull elephant, is acclimatized to hard winters and enjoys playing in the snow with his keeper.

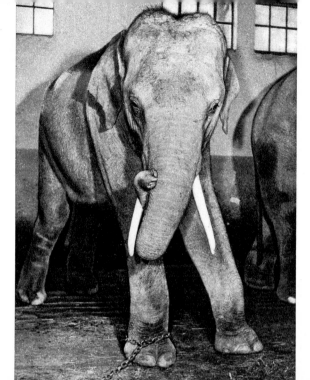

Siam, an Indian elephant, was born with nerves of steel and an easy-going disposition. These natural gifts determined his role in the circus. In the grand finale, he stood in the centre of the ring on a raised stand and solemnly turned himself round while men waved flags, and white ponies, zebras and Norwegian horses circled round him. He did not mind this seething whirl in the very least.

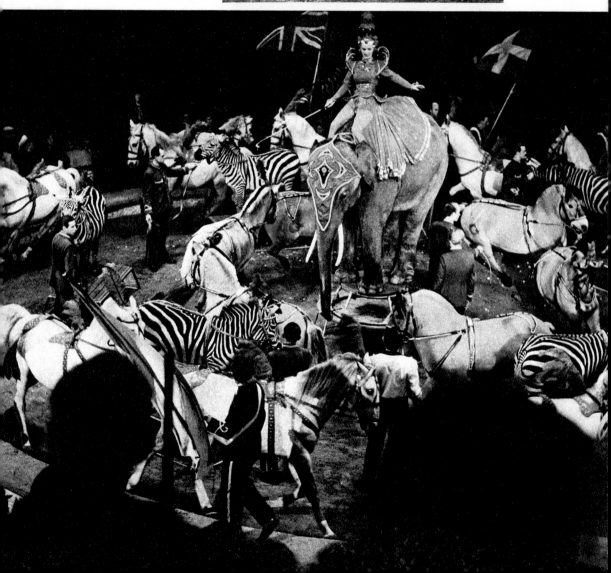

Supposing this vast hoof should come down on top of me... Sandra stands with her left foot poised above me. I have never seen an elephant's foot from this angle before. She must have trodden on a nail at some time. In this position I was completely at her mercy. I had just seen how the elephant had refused to step over a horse lying on the ground, as part of an act which was being worked on for Knie's Circus.

Encouraged by an experience I had had with Sandra when I was on my own with her some days earlier, I decided to try out this test with her and I was keen to photograph such an unusual angle.

African elephants can pick up the most improbable objects with their trunks. An Indian elephant ▶
has only one "finger" on the upper side of its trunk. By contrast, an African has two "fingers"
which enable it to hold on to round objects by suction and, when trained, it can even blow a
French horn.

Below: The Indian elephant, Minjak, danced Rock 'n Roll because she was ticklish.

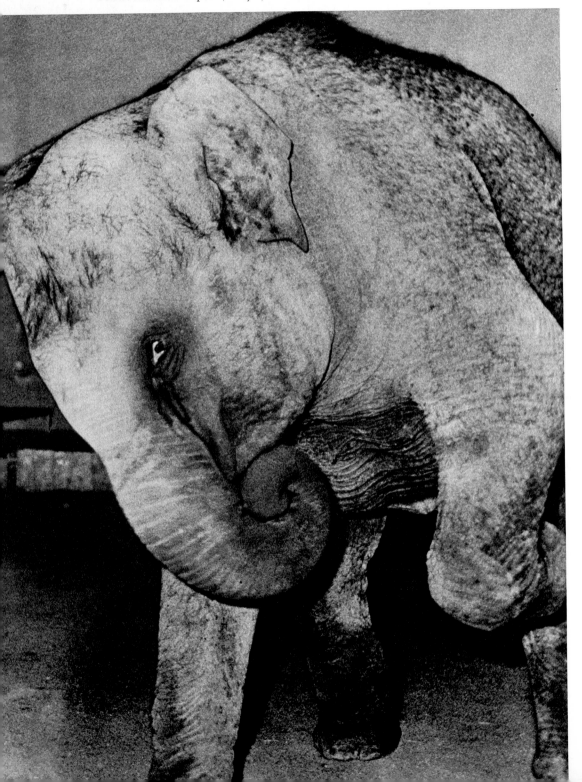

Rosa carried a circus child carefully between her jaws.

The animal trainer Hack can make all kinds of demands on the good=natured Siam.

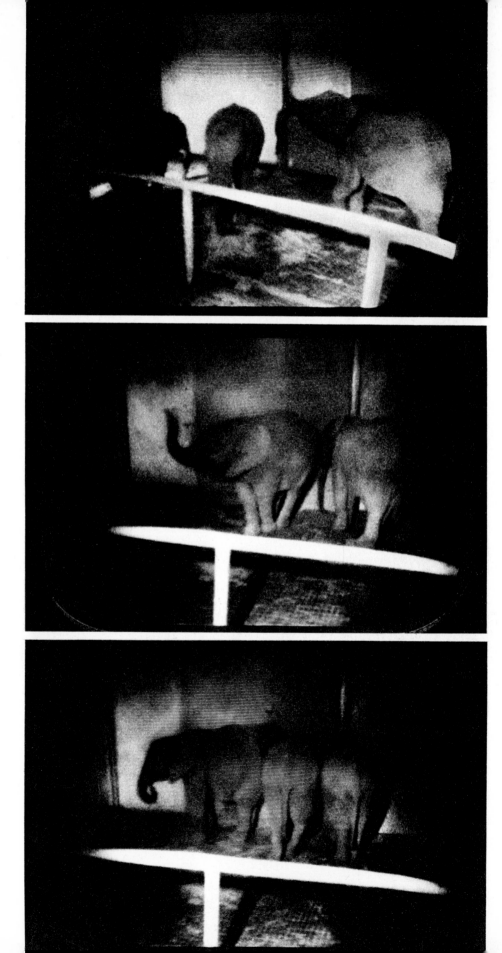

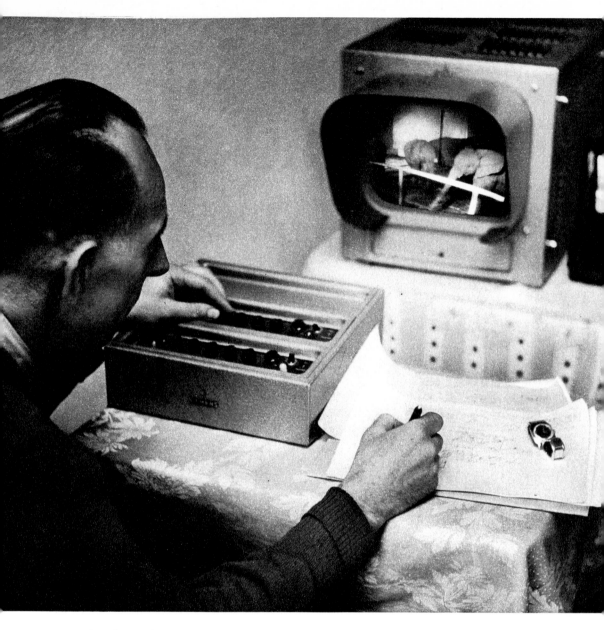

During their first night in a new house in the Kronberg Reserve, the three African elephants were kept under observation by means of an infra=red television camera. Out of the pitch darkness of the elephant den, pictures were thrown on to television monitors enabling observations to be made on their behaviour without in any way disturbing the animals by the presence of humans. Notes were kept of their behaviour and the scenes were photographed from the tele= vision screen.

The three pictures on the left show how the elephants, after wandering about for hours, finally formed up under the leadership of Opeline to have a short sleep.

When captive animals are kept in extensive surroundings, such as in the Kronberg Reserve, they often behave in a way which is not so very different from when they are in the wild. They may thus get into situations which would be impossible in the restricted space available in a zoological garden. Augusta, the hippopotamus, crawled under the fence of the elephant paddock one day at noon and took possession of the elephants' pool. It was a smooth bit of trespassing and any unprejudiced bystander would have expected the elephants to drive the hippo away immediately. In fact, they came storming up, trumpeting angrily, but at the edge of the pool they came to a halt, uncertain what to do. They did not rush into the water to drive Augusta out. It was the hippo, completely at home in her natural element, who shot out of the pool like a rocket and attacked the elephants.

Augusta opened her huge rectangular pink mouth and gaped threateningly at the frightened elephants. The intimidating effect of the threat=yawns was underlined each time by snapping her jaws. Opeline, the leader of the three elephants, started a counter=attack with her ears spread, trumpeting and waving her trunk. However, faced with the gaping jaws of the hippo, all her actions broke down pitifully.

Opeline then tried the other tactic of an attacking elephant. She turned round quickly and went at Augusta tail first, so that she could do a lightning turn at the end, delivering a blow with her trunk. But Augusta went to meet her and snapped her jaws only a few inches away from Opeline's tail.

The elephants' anger at the annexation of their bathing pool was quelled by the hippo's snapping jaws. They beat a retreat to their den, following one behind the other. Shortly before this, Opeline snatched up her last weapon. She seized branches and rubber tyres which were lying around as elephant toys and chucked them over her back at the hippo. Augusta stopped in her tracks, looked very surprised at the fusilade and gave up the chase immediately. She rushed back into the pool. Why had the three elephants given up their territory so quickly? Elephants are nomadic and do not defend territory. Hippos, on the other hand, are faithful to a locality. They have a sense of property and will defend it. This is what Augusta was doing with the pool and its surroundings.

136

Augusta was unwilling to leave the pool. She could be chased away only by an alsatian.

Augusta rests from her adventure, which otherwise could have happened only in the wild.

CHAPTER 11

Elephants after Dark

It was a frosty January morning at the Kronberg Reserve for Animal Research on the south slopes of the Taunus. A damp grey mist lay over the reserve and from the window of a small conference room the shadowy outlines of the animals looked like ghosts from another world as they tramped about in the snow. A group of us had been sitting in this room for hours holding a lengthy discussion without reaching any conclusion. There were the Curator of the Reserve, Dr Georg von Opel, several animal behaviour research workers and some of the keepers. I was also present as a journalist interested in zoology.

In a few days' time three African elephants were due to be moved into new quarters in the reserve and there was considerable speculation as to how they would react when introduced to the extensive paddock with its new stable. When one bears in mind that elephants are both intelligent and inquisitive, as well as immense=ly strong, their reaction to new surroundings was important from all points of view and no one was quite certain what would happen. The main controversy centred on one particular point: assuming that all went well, would it not be wiser, nevertheless, to keep them chained up at night? The Curator was well known for his views on the necessity for conducting experiments with the animals kept under conditions of the greatest possible freedom; he spoke out flatly against any fettering of the elephants and said that it would ruin his plans; in this kind of work some risks must be taken. One member of his staff, on the other hand, thought that the risk was too great, bearing in mind what elephants can do, and he pointed out that no zoo or circus allowed their elephants to go unchained at night. The argument and discussion continued. Questions were raised to which no answers could be given. The speculation was very interesting to the detached onlooker but to the zoologists and the keepers it contained an element of danger. We continued to think aloud. If only there were some method of keeping a watch on the ele=phants at night without their being aware of the observers; then there would be no need to chain them at all. We stared blankly out of the window into the mist.

Suddenly I thought of television: could one not install it for this purpose? Twenty=four hours later the technicians from Siemens were at Kronberg. They said that, apart from underwater work, television cameras had not been used previously for observing animals. The zoologists at the reserve knew of no such case and we were therefore breaking fresh ground. We set to work, installing the equipment, with an enthusiasm which even the bitterly cold weather did not affect.

Working with infra=red lights and cameras, we planned to get pictures which would be as clear as daylight on our screens without a single ray of light being visible in the elephant house. The elephants would be quite undisturbed while we watched what they were doing on our television screens, completely shut off in an office some hundreds of yards away. Assuming that everything worked as it should, we would be able to observe how the elephants spent their first night in new surroundings, how they divided up the available space perhaps, and whether they slept standing up or lying down. The plan was for a written record of obser= vations to be kept throughout the night and I would make a pictorial record of the various scenes by taking photographs directly from the television screen. At the same time the elephants would be virtually under our control because if they showed signs of starting any trouble we could move in at once.

Little research had been done previously on the sleep of animals and the infra= red cameras would make it possible to penetrate this field. Two cameras would be in use simultaneously: one, with a wide=angle lens, would take a picture of the entire area inside the den; the other, with a telephoto lens, would take close= up pictures and, by means of remote control, would follow the movements of indi= vidual animals, showing them in detail. This was our plan of action and we then decided to go one better and put a microphone into the stable, set at a low sensi= tivity so that it picked up any abnormal level of noise from the elephants. It would be effective, for instance, if the elephants trumpeted or if they started demolishing the place. The microphone was connected to an alarm mechanism which rang in the Curator's bedroom, even farther away from the elephants than our observa= tion post. When the alarm went off the Curator had only to switch on the tele= vision monitor by his bed to see what the elephants were actually doing.

We were very excited when everything was ready, hoping that all the appa= ratus would work. Before the elephants were due to move we decided to do a test run with the equipment on the ibex enclosure. We tried it out by day and at night. And our first surprise came when we tested the infra=red equipment at night. We switched on: the searchlight and the camera moved across the scene in the pad= dock. What was that? Spots of light looking rather like glow=worms danced across the picture on our screen. Could it be interference? No. Then all at once strangely glowing creatures from another planet turned into our homely ibex — the "glow= worms" were in fact the eyes of the ibex following the movement of our camera= man, who was standing on the roof above us, overlooking the paddock.

The zoologists were immediately full of questions. Why should the eyes of the ibex reflect the infra=red light so strongly? Human eyes do not react to infra=red, we do not see it. Could it be that an ibex sees infra=red light? Was there a reflection from the back of the eye? Are all animals sensitive to infra=red light? If not, which ones, and why some and not others? While this was going on I succeeded in photo= graphing the ghostly picture of our first nocturnal experiment with infra=red.

When the day came for moving the elephants we were so excited that we forgot about the possible dangers and could hardly bear the suspense of waiting for nightfall. The office had been made as comfortable as possible, with camp beds and blankets available. The zoologist Dr Theodor Haltenorth was to make obser= vations and keep a log while I took photographs of the screens. Pencils, paper, watch, camera, everything was ready.

The elephants took possession of their new paddock during the morning. Their move in was uneventful but they hesitated for a long time before actually setting foot inside the den and spent an hour standing at the entrance with their trunks up like live periscopes. Eventually they ventured in and walked all round, probing with their tusks and investigating the walls and floor with their trunks, inspecting everything within reach. For the first time in the history of elephant=keeping a hanging door had been installed. In no time the elephants discovered how it worked and it only took them a few minutes to find out that they could enter and leave the house as they liked. Knowing that there was a way of escape open to them, they did not feel captive or hemmed in and this removed much of their nervousness in the new surroundings.

Twilight came early on the Taunus slopes and it was bitterly cold outside. We made a last check on the equipment in the elephant den; everything was safely out of reach of inquisitive trunks. Large bundles of hay were put down in the hope that this would help the elephants to settle down, and when it was completely dark we left them. A biting east wind hit us as we came out of the den. The ground was frozen. We hurried back over the slippery surface as fast as we could to our observation post. Now our only link with the elephants was through cables.

We switched on, pressed the buttons and turned the knobs. There was the usual crackling: white flashes, streaks and dots appeared on the screen. We adjusted our monitors: horizontal and vertical hold, brightness, contrast . . . and there they were, our three elephants. They were still roaming about in the den, exploring everything with their trunks. Although they were in complete darkness, we could see them quite clearly as they moved about testing and sniffing at everything. There was something rather uncanny about watching animals feeling their way about blindly in the dark and yet looking on our screens as though they were in bright light. As far as we were concerned the darkness provided no cloak of invis= ibility.

A picture converter was the magic box which made it possible for us to see the infra=red pictures. Infra=red rays were projected by a searchlight on to the objects under observation and were reflected back just like ordinary light waves. The re= flected rays were focused on the picture converter by a special lens. On the side of the converter facing the elephants, sensitive photo=electric cells transmitted signals through a valve system to the rear screen of the converter, where a fluores= cent black=and=white reproduction of the infra=red signal, correctly balanced for light and shade, was produced. This picture was then transmitted by the television camera to the monitors.

The elephant log was full of entries. Each page was an apparent confusion of lines and numerals with the appropriate time of night against each entry. Shortly after three o'clock the confusion sorted itself out and the lines all led in one di= rection: the elephants were at last going to sleep.

On our screens we saw quite clearly how the social hierarchy was strictly ad= hered to by night as well as by day. The leader of the small group was a female elephant called Opeline. The two younger bulls spent a long time wandering about and playing with the hanging door but shortly after three o'clock in the morning Opeline sent them firmly to bed. It was a remarkable performance. After repeated= ly examining the entire area of the den, she pushed the two bulls into a corner; it was not just any old corner but the one which appeared to be the safest, and she then went on watch. Soon we saw the younger elephants rolling up their trunks and leaning against each other, a sure sign that they had fallen into a deep sleep. This sleep, however, only lasted for three hours because their fast metabolism made it necessary for them to evacuate their bowels. We also saw how they swayed from side to side when asleep, maintaining a gentle rhythm, relieving each leg with steady regularity. During all this time Opeline remained wide awake, obviously listening to every sound. It was not long before she moved over to the swing door, making it work so that she could put her trunk out and scent the cold winter's night; then she would return to the sleeping elephants and finger them with her trunk. Finally, in the early hours of the morning, she stood close to the others but facing in the opposite direction, with her head pointing towards the side from which disturbance would first come — namely, the door through which we had disappeared the previous evening. Then her trunk appeared to retract somewhat and she went into a light sleep. Her senses, however, were not quies= cent and she was ready to respond in a fraction of a second to any sign of danger.

At last dawn showed through the window. Our watches told us it was a few minutes past six as the buckets clattered in the yard where the keepers were already at work. Our eyes ached and smarted. After ten hours of viewing television we were exhausted but triumphant. The result of our first use of infra=red television for observing animals showed that the way was now open for investigating many unexplained mysteries.

CHAPTER 12

Augusta's Take-over Bid

THE ELEPHANTS WERE one of the show-pieces of the open reserve, but running them a close second was a hippopotamus called Augusta. There was a time, be= fore George arrived to keep her company, when she was the sole occupant of very comfortable quarters which included a heated indoor pool as well as an outside one. Like the elephants, Augusta could decide for herself whether to be inside or out, as she also had a new=style hanging door. She had learned quickly how to use it. In spite of her massive bulk and slow appearance Augusta was not stupid. At one time I had quite a lot to do with her and although she appeared to be dominated by the urge to feed she gave me the impression of having the mental capacity of a fairly gifted dog plus the craftiness of a sow and the placidity of a cow. All this was only so long as Augusta and I were in complete agreement as to what we should do next. When our opinions differed she had two ways of showing her dislike of my ideas: she either became as obstinate as a mule or she attacked with a gaping mouth. Usually a hint of one of these expressions of ill humour was sufficient for my ideas to be either nipped in the bud or put into cold storage. In spite of this we enjoyed going out together and when I opened the door of her paddock she always came up to me snorting with pleasure.

One hot summer's day I went to fetch Augusta for a walk in the lunch hour. On this occasion we were not alone. We wanted to go rather a long way to a meadow which lay alongside the elephant paddock, and so Herr Dohse, who was in charge of all the animals, came with us.

My massive girl=friend much appreciated a wide path or verge so that she could linger on the way, spinning out her walk for a nice long time. As we set out I was already thinking ahead to the moment when I would have to persuade her that it would be a good idea to start the return journey, and working out how long it would take us to come to terms about it. When dealing with animals I always allowed plenty of time and I had chosen to go on this particular walk during the lunch hour for a good reason. To get to the meadow it was necessary to use a public path, and few people would be entering the reserve at this time because it was too hot at midday. In any case it is not everyone who would expect to meet a hippopotamus on a philosophical stroll between Bad Königstein and Kronberg.

It was very warm and Augusta appeared to be sweating. There were glistening drops of moisture, like red beads, exuding from her pores. But the sweating could just as well have been caused by excitement as by heat, because Augusta was ex=ploring new country and I had frequently noticed that when she was excited red beads of moisture appeared.

When we reached the meadow it occurred to me that a hippo from Africa grazing in an unfenced field, just like a cow put out to pasture, was sufficiently out of the ordinary to warrant photographing and I took Augusta's portrait in black=and=white and in colour. It was all very peaceful. Herr Dohse and I had a great deal to talk over and with Augusta grazing contentedly we finally forgot all about her. I remember being aware at one stage of a peculiar scraping sound coming from my left somewhere but I paid no particular attention to it. This went on for a short while until suddenly it was so loud that we could not fail to notice it. Herr Dohse stopped short and listened. We both spun round and our eyes came to rest on the perimeter fence of the elephant paddock. We were just in time to see Augusta squeezing through the double fence on her belly. The portly hippo had succeeded in making herself sufficiently small and flat to get under the fence. It was the coarse hippo skin rasping like a file on the metal fence which we had heard.

We rushed over but it was impossible to make Augusta either stop or turn back. We shouted at her: "Back, back," and waved our arms but she paid not the slightest attention. It was too late. She struggled to free her last fold of fat and with a mighty heave she was free, right inside the elephant enclosure. We shot under the fence and ran ahead of her so that we could try to bar the way with out=stretched arms. But Augusta was not to be distracted and she came relentlessly towards us, not wavering from her course in the slightest. She snapped her powerful jaws at us angrily and I saw right down her pink throat as she gave her best threat display. A hippo bite has broken many a man's bones. Augusta was not to be trifled with in this mood and we both sprang to one side. She knew where she was going and nothing was going to stop her. Stubbornly she pushed ahead like a huge tank forcing its way across country. She had a quite definite goal: the sparkling water of the elephants' pool. She reached the edge and with a lot of blowing and splashing launched herself into her native element. We were in serious trouble.

During the first excitement we had failed to notice the elephants and we now saw them trotting out to the attack, leaving their stable where they had retreated for their midday siesta. They were one behind the other with Opeline in the lead, trumpeting in anger. The two bulls joined in the uproar. Their ears stood out sideways and they ran with their trunks up like periscopes as they tested the scent of the stranger ahead of them. There seemed to be no point in trying to stop the uproar and it would scarcely have been wise to try to make a stand between the angry combatants. Neither Herr Dohse nor I had any wish to be trampled underfoot and we decided that whatever happened discretion was the better part of valour. And so we promptly took to our heels and ran.

It was at this point that I suddenly remembered my two cameras hanging round

my neck. So far I had not got a single picture of this unusual situation. In re=
trospect I wished particularly that I had taken Augusta squeezing under the fence,
but when it was actually happening all I could think of was how to prevent her
from getting to the elephants, so that today I lack pictures of the beginning part
of this exciting sequence of events.

Opeline came storming down to the water to deliver her attack. Snorting and
blowing she trumpeted with shrill screams, stamping and shuffling her feet so
that the dust flew. Vauka and Conti, the two bulls, stood a little farther off and
waited. This was a familiar situation: it was always Opeline who was the first to
make any kind of move. In the early years the initiative was taken exclusively by
the female; the youngsters always watched from the background. At the pool they
remained behind Opeline, providing support by trumpeting angrily.

Augusta stood in the pool up to her neck, watching the display with interest,
but she did not appear to be at all impressed by it. She certainly showed no fear
of the three grey giants. I should mention here that these animals had never seen
one another before and none of them had previously made the acquaintance of any
member of the other species. Their behaviour was in no way the result of pre=
vious experience. Everything that they did must therefore have been unlearnt. The
involuntary encounter of these two powerful species was terrifying to witness.
We felt small and helpless. Although we were slightly scared on our own account,
our main concern was for the animals. The three elephants were strong enough
to crush the hippopotamus.

"I'll run and fetch the others," shouted Herr Dohse, "we must separate them."
He ran off towards the mess=room where the keepers were having their lunch.
I stayed behind, feeling very much alone. But what happened next completely
took my breath away. As the three elephants assembled, apparently preparing for
a concerted attack, Augusta suddenly rushed out of the water, like a torpedo from
a submarine, and landed immediately in front of Opeline's legs. The huge ele=
phant let out a piercing scream and took fright, retreating a couple of yards. This
had taken her completely by surprise. She waved her trunk defensively in the air
and although she could easily have struck the hippo with it, she did not venture
to do so. She appeared to be thoroughly shocked. The two bulls reacted immediate=
ly: Conti backed away from the source of danger, pushing Vauka back. Suddenly
all three were stricken with panic by the sight of Augusta, who looked like a wet
barrel and behaved as though she felt perfectly safe inside her thick skin. Embol=
dened by her victory, she attacked again. I could scarcely believe my eyes. Augusta
was actually driving the elephants off their own home ground. She apparently
had no feeling of being in strange territory. What made the elephants afraid of
chasing the cheeky intruder out of their own paddock?

Opeline then started a counter=attack. She trotted up and down several times,
broadside on to Augusta, trumpeting and waving her ears and trunk as though
to encourage herself She turned suddenly through ninety degrees and, snorting

loudly, she stormed at the hippo. Opeline had all the advantages and I was sure
that this would be the reprisal. Augusta had no means of protection, she could
only take flight. I looked round for Herr Dohse and the others. At least he had
left the big gate open, directly behind Augusta, and if only she would run for it,
this might save her life.

Opeline charged like an express train at the hippo. Rolling in fat, Augusta
personified calm resignation. She did not budge an inch. In fact, she did nothing
at all except open her powerful jaws and show her sparkling canines. Opeline
could easily have taken a swipe at Augusta with her trunk, the hippo was now
well within her range, but Opeline seemed to waver. She appeared to be dazed
by the gaping mouth. Augusta's threat was a thousand times more effective
than all the display of anger from the elephant. Opeline wheeled round on
her hind=quarters within a few inches of Augusta. Was she feigning a frontal
attack and preparing to attack from the rear? Elephants will sometimes do
this. Then Augusta shot forwards, roaring the battle cry of all hippos, her
mouth wide open. Opeline's trumpeting fanfare petered out into a laughable
squeak and she swung the long=haired tuft of her tail high. A fraction of a second
later Augusta snapped her jaws. And immediately the fighting morale of the
elephant ebbed away. Without showing any resistance she allowed Augusta to
drive her round the pool. Opeline made one last demonstration: as she fled in
front of the hippo, she saw loose branches and a rubber tyre which was an
elephant toy lying on the ground. She seized them and flung them over her back
in Augusta's direction. Augusta stopped abruptly. She suddenly gave up the
pursuit of the elephants, trotted smartly back to the pool and splashed into the
water — because this is where a hippo feels safest.

This seemed to satisfy the elephants and in any case they had had enough.
They rushed into the stable, one behind the other in their usual order: Opeline in
front, then Conti and the youngest, Vauka, bringing up the rear with his tail erect.
Augusta celebrated her victory with a frog's eye view of the fleeing elephants as
she rested low in the water.

The keepers came running up and I breathed a sigh of relief. Herr Dohse was
out of breath as he shut the elephant stable door and the keepers, armed with
sticks and poles, whips and giant brooms, stood by. And I noticed once again the
red beads of moisture on the pores of Augusta's skin.

But this was not the end of the story. Augusta began to feel thoroughly at
home in the pool which did not belong to her and she ignored our invitation to
leave this beautiful lido. Why should she leave the pool which she had succeeded in
capturing? She dived.

Research has shown that a hippo can remain under water from four to six
minutes and, if necessary, up to fifteen minutes. Augusta, needless to say,
treated it as an emergency and we waited an eternity before our spherical lady
emerged, puffing and blowing and spraying us all with water. She twitched her
ears, shaking out the last drops of water. We immediately held out a turnip

in front of her, which she took without hesitation. In this way we enticed her out of the pool. Then a couple of stout=hearted keepers thumped her hind= quarters with giant brooms in an effort to encourage her to leave the elephant paddock. But we had reckoned without her sense of possession. Augusta remem= bered her number=one method of getting her own way with humans and she sat herself down. Nothing would persuade her to move now. She ignored the titbits held in front of her nose and just remained sitting. She was only a few yards from the open gate in the fence and if we had only been able to push her a couple of steps forward we would have won. It was a ridiculous scene. We all stood round her looking at the mountain of flesh. We dared not move lest she should snatch the opportunity of breaking through the blockade and rush back to the elephant's pool.

Once again we were faced with the inevitable question which confronts all animal keepers: what was to be done? Various possibilities were suggested. A jet of water? The nearest hydrant was too far away. A mild electric shock? It seemed that all our ideas would take too long to put into action. And then, by chance, Herr Dohse suddenly noticed the Curator's dog wandering about. He was a large alsatian called Astor and he came bounding along, wagging his tail.

The hippo became restless as she scented him. "Fetch it, Astor, fetch it, here," instructed Herr Dohse as he slapped Augusta's solid rump with the flat of his hand. Astor needed no encouragement and he went straight for her hind=quarters, growling and giving short barks. Augusta got to her feet with astonishing agility and, prodded by Astor's nose, she started to walk very unwillingly. The dog gave her no chance to pause; as soon as she looked round, he was at her heels again. Having routed three elephants, Augusta resigned herself to the inevitable and trotted home at the behest of a mere dog.

At first sight it may seem strange that the hippo could put elephants to flight on their own home ground. In fact the answer is quite simple. Elephants in the wild have no well=defined territory within fixed boundaries. They have favoured places but they are nomadic and generally speaking do not stick to a particular area. They move from place to place in search of food and in the dry season they undertake long journeys to water holes which do not dry up. Here they collect into giant herds which break up into smaller groups again in the wet season.

Hippos, on the other hand, have quite different habits and are faithful to one locality. On land they have a pear=shaped territory which stems from their resting place in the water. They have a well=developed sense of property and mark their territory by spreading their faeces with their tail. The water is where they feel most secure and this place of refuge must be kept free from intruders.

To speak of Augusta's courage and the cowardice of the three elephants is neither here nor there. Both species of animal behaved naturally: the one yielded ground because it had no drive to defend either land or water; the other defended both land and water because both such places are essential to the survival of its kind.

CHAPTER 13

When Elephants Tremble

COLOGNE ZOO CELEBRATED its centenary in 1960 and to mark the occasion the postal authorities of this cathedral city issued a special stamp with an original design. It showed a large elephant panicking when confronted by a tiny little mouse. To the average person the scene depicted is either make=believe or so grossly exaggerated as to be an amusing caricature. The layman accepts it with a smile and thinks that the zoo has got a good advertisement based on a fable or legend. He would be very surprised indeed to learn that the stamp illustrated a mystery of elephant behaviour which is still unsolved.

The story is not new to experts and it still fascinates the layman, and if he were to ask an expert why the elephant should be panic=stricken when confronted by a small animal, the expert could not give him an answer. Nobody knows on what this fear is based. Zoologists and behaviour students have conducted many experiments in this field. A wide variety of small animals have been placed in front of elephants and, apart from certain local variations, they have all established one fact: elephants are extremely worried by small animals. We do not know any more than this. Experiments have also shown that elephants in a zoo or circus will look at a mouse inquisitively and then kill it. One must remember that these elephants have two feet tethered and that they have no choice, they can only attack the repugnant creature and tread on it; they cannot run away although they would undoubtedly prefer to do so. For instance, the chains were removed from an elephant which had just killed a white mouse in her stall; she was taken outside and presented with another white mouse and, free to choose how to deal with the situation, she retreated immediately.

When I began to take an interest in the subject I was not breaking any fresh ground from the scientific point of view. Pure chance suddenly drew my attention to the subject and I looked forward to the photographic possibilities which it might offer. As a layman I had no intention of ferreting out information which the experts had so far failed to uncover. I merely decided to keep my eyes open. Previous investigations on this subject had all been made on animals in captivity, either in zoos or circuses.

The fact that elephants also dislike small creatures in the wild was proved to me by an observation made by Eberhard Trumler, the zoologist in the Kronberg Reserve. It is worth emphasizing that in this Reserve animals are free to move about unhindered in an extensive area and so behave naturally according to their species. Late one afternoon Trumler was squatting near the elephants, watching them playing and feeding. Opeline suddenly gave a short warning cry without any apparent cause. Something was obviously worrying her. She stretched her trunk far out in front of her down into the grass and then audibly drew in air as she took the scent. At the same time she flapped her ears, which stuck out sideways from her head like huge sails. Then she rumbled and snorted. Conti and Vauka came up but remained watching at a respectful distance, their ears also held out at right angles and their trunks sucking up and testing the air suspiciously. Trumler wondered what it could be and he stood up to try to get a better view. From his position he could see nothing to cause unrest. Nevertheless something was undoubtedly moving in the grass because the elephants' heads, particularly their trunks, were distinctly following some movement. The three elephants were obviously unhappy about it, judging from their reactions. They were rather a pathetic sight. Opeline then trumpeted again, turned on her heel and trotted back to the stable as fast as she could go, with the other two following.

Trumler had marked the exact spot in the grass and he ran over to see if he could find something which might have caused such peculiar behaviour. He did not have to search long: a hedgehog was taking its afternoon stroll in the elephants' paddock. Trumler knew of an elephant's fear of a mouse and he was familiar with the research of his colleagues in this field. Nevertheless, it was a strange experience to witness such an incident. He shook his head and decided to take the hedgehog which had routed three elephants back to his office.

It so happened that I turned up at the Reserve only a few days later and Herr Trumler told me of his experience. We were in his office and I asked him if he still had the hedgehog. "Can't you hear it?" he replied. I listened. There was a scratching noise under the desk. The hedgehog had just been given its evening meal of minced meat, earthworms and raisins. It was an attractive little creature, only a youngster, with its spines not yet completely hard. It rolled into a ball as soon as I lifted it up, a sure sign that it was not accustomed to the human hand. Tame hedgehogs get to know that there is no danger and no longer roll up. It appeared to be quite happy on the palm of my hand; a lively army of fleas jumped about between its spines. It is no good trying to scratch yourself if you are a hedge=hog unless you are prepared to be impaled on your own spines. The fleas appear to take advantage of this and work down near the base of the spines. It seems as though a hedgehog does not itch, it behaves as though all is well — otherwise its life would certainly be unbearable.

It was hard to believe that such an inoffensive creature could have upset three elephants. I was very keen to try it out again. Eberhard Trumler was quite happy to do so and we set off for the elephant paddock, taking the elephant goad with us in case of need. It was already getting dark as we arrived and the light was poor. But I was so curious to see what would happen that I could not wait until the morning. I wanted to see for myself whether elephants were as frightened as they were reported to be.

The three elephants were standing out of doors in front of their stable when we got there. I crept under the fence and quickly put the hedgehog down on the cement directly between the elephants and the entrance to their house. The hedgehog was rolled up into a prickly ball. While it remained rolled up the elephants fingered it with their trunks, picking up its scent. But the moment it came to life and unrolled, there was a violent change in the elephants' behaviour: within a few seconds they trumpeted and fled in terror. They moved as far from the uncanny object as they could possibly get and would probably have gone right out of sight of the hedgehog had the fence not been in the way. Fortunately we had shut the gate between the outer and inner paddock or we would have lost them from view altogether. The hedgehog ran about quite actively, investigating the lie of the land; it showed no fear of the trampling grey columns which gave way every time it approached them. It looked to me as though the elephants often shook with physical aversion. Opeline's terror knew no bounds, she even tried to get over the fence. The elephants followed every movement which the hedgehog made, adjusting their position accordingly and looking in all directions for some escape. The only possible escape route was in through the open door of their house but the hedgehog blocked the way by patrolling up and down in front of it. At one moment, however, it moved a little farther away, thus removing the psychological blockade; the elephants seized the opportunity and went into their den as fast as they could.

The hedgehog had served its purpose and we put it back into its shoebox. Herr Trumler decided to take it home with him to Munich and he prophesied a great future for it, with a star=billing on television. And so it came about that the little hedgehog, victor of a contest with three elephants, became the hero of a fifteen=minute television programme. As I told the story of its prowess, Herr Trumler sat beside me in the studio and at the appropriate moment he undid his brief=case and produced the hedgehog hero in person.

I wondered what the basis of this terror of small animals could be. When the elephants were young I saw them attack small dogs, brought into the reserve by visitors, without any hesitation. At the time of the hedgehog incident they were older and showed no fear of small dogs. What constitutes the threshold of their terror? Has it something to do with the legs of small animals? Are movements always slightly blurred for elephants? If so, a small body which apparently moved without any limbs to propel it might seem strange and therefore alarming.

Four years after the incident with the hedgehog I decided to look into the problem more closely and conduct a series of observations on my own. I wanted to do five experiments. All the necessary items were ready: four white mice, a guinea=pig, a dummy hedgehog, a stuffed mechanical toy dog which jumped, and a real live snake. I planned to start with the live snake, the animal without legs, but as I started to open the linen bag I had second thoughts. Supposing the elephant came up to the snake, testing it for scent, and the snake bit it on the trunk? The elephant might panic and get injured. I decided at the last moment that my snake experiment was too risky and re=tied the tapes of the bag securely.

The idea of showing white mice to elephants was not my own and there was nothing new in it. The last experiments of this kind known to me were undertaken many years earlier and were carried out with the mice tied by their tails and the elephants chained. I had thought of a simple device for my experiment which would enable elephants and mice to mix freely together. I placed a circular plastic container on the concrete of the small paddock which the three African elephants used in the winter; the walls of the container were low but sufficiently high to prevent the mice from jumping out. I released the four white mice inside the plastic walls. I assumed that this device would keep the mice within the circle but that, when the elephants discovered the mice could not get out, they would come nearer and probably overturn the plastic container with their trunks. In this way the mice would be released without human interference and I would be able to observe the natural reactions of the elephants.

The elephants were shut in the den while we installed the mice. I then climbed a tall ladder so that I would have an unrestricted view overlooking the paddock and could operate my cameras without interference. Opeline pushed up the door, the other two pressing behind her. All three stopped dead in their tracks near the door, as though they were rivetted to the ground. They had seen my plastic device with the mice scuttling about in it. After the initial shock they took up positions alongside one another as though for briefing. They stood shoulder to shoulder and stared at the enemy, extending their trunks as far forward as they could reach, testing and sucking in the scent of the mice. They flapped their ears to and fro continuously, making a kind of air pocket within which the strange scent was concentrated. After a certain amount of time they realized that, although the mice were active, they did not come out, and the two bulls approached the plastic con= tainer with great care, rather like advance scouts spying out the land. I was aston= ished to see that Opeline took no part in this reconnaissance but drew back into a corner of the paddock and waited. She had quite openly relinquished her leader= ship. Conti and Vauka "fingered" the transparent plastic wall, blowing down their trunks, while the mice jumped around in the centre. These two showed no fear. Was this because they could see the legs of the mice? Suddenly Conti blew very hard against the plastic wall and, just as I had hoped, the frail structure collapsed, setting the mice free.

At first the two bulls stood there completely petrified, as though they could not understand what had happened. Then they shot away in full flight to the farthest corner of their paddock. They pressed so hard against the fence that it was as though an unseen force had driven them into the corner. The giants trembled as they watched the white mice scuttling along the ground. They stamped and shuffled their feet, as though they did not know where to tread; if there had been sand on the ground instead of concrete, they would have showered the mice with it. They turned their hind=quarters towards the white peril, only turning around now and again to see where the midget army had got to. As though to give himself more security, Conti hung his trunk over the other side of the iron fence. The mice ran hither and thither over the cement and there was no doubt that the paddock belonged to them and not to the elephants.

Conti was the first to lose his nerve. With extended gait he tried to reach the open doorway to the den, but it was not to be. When he was only half=way there, an inquisitive mouse tripped into the den through the open door. Conti froze in his tracks and let out a high=pitched scream. His whole body trembled and his ears went flat against his head like withered leaves. A tiny mouse which he could have squashed to death with just one tread of his powerful foot prevented him from reaching his den — the place where he felt safest of all as a captive animal. What was it about the mouse that he found so sinister?

We retrieved the mice and had a short rest. For the second experiment we put out the plastic container again but this time with a guinea=pig. The device was no longer new to the elephants and this was a distinct disadvantage. In addition something else happened which I had not reckoned with: because of its fear of the elephants the guinea=pig became aggressive.

I returned to my look=out post on the ladder. The elephants were let out of their house. I should not have underestimated their cunning: the crafty creatures re=membered that when they blew on the plastic sides of the container it had done them no good, and this time they took great care not to let their trunks get too close to it. They all took it in turns, including Opeline, to go up to the guinea=pig and stand with their trunks above it, holding its scent and inspecting it thoroughly. All their movements appeared to be very deliberate. They were on the alert and ready to move away, although they showed no obvious signs of fear. They had discovered that everything was quite harmless, providing the plastic walls re=mained upright. The parade of the elephants alarmed the guinea=pig, which spat at them in fright. This high=pitched spitting was not a sound with which the ele=phants were familiar. It was possible that it meant danger, and so, one by one, they turned around and retreated to their house, going faster as their courage ebbed. Conti was the first to move, then Opeline and last of all Vauka, who seemed to have taken over the role of leader. Once again the elephants seemed to find flight the safest method of ridding themselves of an unwelcome creature, even though one step would have trampled it to death.

The third experiment started with a dummy hedgehog on the ground. I bought an unpainted rubber ball, cut it in half and stuck small toothpicks into it. I was well aware that the dummy had no animal smell of any kind and this could well be a disadvantage; in fact it reeked of artificiality but as it turned out the smell of the rubber played no significant role. I tied a nylon thread to my "hedgehog" to enable it to be pulled along the ground and two men stood by to operate it.

The elephants came out and stopped: they flapped their ears and formed up, ready to gather information. This was all just the same as in the two previous experiments. I gave the signal for the operation of the dummy but nothing hap= pened. When the string was twitched the dummy did not move. In fact it could not move because Vauka was standing on the nylon thread. We could only wait patiently, hoping that Vauka would change his position and that none of the others would stand on the thread. The trunks moved towards the motionless rubber hedgehog. They could not make it out, its shape and attitude were in no sense familiar to the elephants, neither did it move. From the elephants' point of view it was dull and uninteresting, not worth bothering about, and Vauka stepped to one side. As soon as he had moved off the thread, the dummy hedgehog started to joggle about on the ground. This was a decisive moment in the experi= ment. Horrified, the elephants fled. Once again they stood in the corner, prisoners in their own paddock all over again. The dummy continued to shuffle about. And then something happened. Vauka began to finger the ground with his trunk. "He has got my thread!" shouted one of my assistants. I shall never believe anyone again who says that elephants have poor eyesight. The thread was so fine that we could hardly see it. In his role as leader Vauka was acting as watch= dog and in this way he discovered the thread. He wound it round his trunk, thus making the dummy move. He was unwittingly helping me in my experiment and it became a kind of game for him. Every time he shuffled the thread about, the dummy hedgehog gave a little hop. This made the other two elephants so ner= vous that they started to cast sidelong glances at the open door. Then Vauka noticed that every time he jerked the thread the thing came nearer to him. It was no longer a game, the thing was sinister. He suddenly let go of the thread and stormed off, the others following behind. It was an absurd result and certainly not one that I had anticipated.

We needed the nylon thread for the last experiment and so we wound it in, removed the rubber hedgehog and fastened the thread to a toy dog. I had spent a long time in a Frankfurt toyshop looking for the right model. I finally chose a black cloth poodle with movable legs that were specially well constructed. It mea= sured four and a half inches from head to foot and the length of its legs was about two inches — about half an inch longer than those of the guinea=pig. The length of the legs was significant as far as I was concerned. By pulling the dog on a string it could be made to look as though it were running, with its legs kicking up behind. It would have been better from the point of view of the ex= periment to use a live dog but only a young puppy would have had the propor= tion of leg to body which I wanted. When they are as young as this puppies are clumsy and helpless. Since the animal might well get killed in the experiment, it would have been inexcusable to use a young live animal.

I wanted to photograph this experiment from a low angle and so I placed my= self close to the fence. The black cloth dog stood in the paddock and the elephants came out. Opeline and Conti held back against the wall of the house while Vauka

Two extremes of posture in the African elephant which show clearly the importance of the ears as a means of expression. The animal on the left is turning round to investigate someone. He raises his head for a moment and spreads his ears wide, increasing his apparent size, and stretches the tip of his trunk forward taking the scent. The elephant on the right is undecided; the lowered trunk tip signifies attack, the back=folded ears flight.

A small hedgehog can cause confusion in a whole herd of elephants. The three African elephants fled in panic one evening when confronted by a hedgehog and they rushed into their house. This made me decide to try some experiments and to photograph them in the process. I was keen to see for myself whether elephants really are afraid of mice.

I placed a circular plastic enclosure on the ground in front of the elephant house and released three white mice into it. The elephants approached my mouse circus cautiously, with their trunks stretched out, sniffing and blowing as they tested the strange scent. The plastic walls suddenly collapsed under the draught of air from the trunks and the mice escaped. The elephants had to deal with a situation which they had themselves created, and this was just what I had hoped for. They drew back in alarm. When one of the mice ran into the elephant house, Vauka stood outside and trembled (see next page).

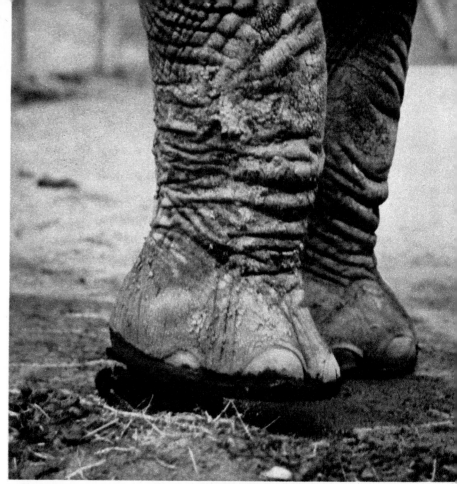

The same elephant behaved quite differently when I made a small toy dog hop along on a nylon thread. Vauka immediately spread his ears, touched his right temporal gland with the tip of his trunk — a sure sign that something would happen — and then attacked the stuffed poodle. He knocked it over with a single blow of his trunk and stamped on it with his right foot. The toy dog cracked under the weight and all that remained was a dirty, flattened mess.

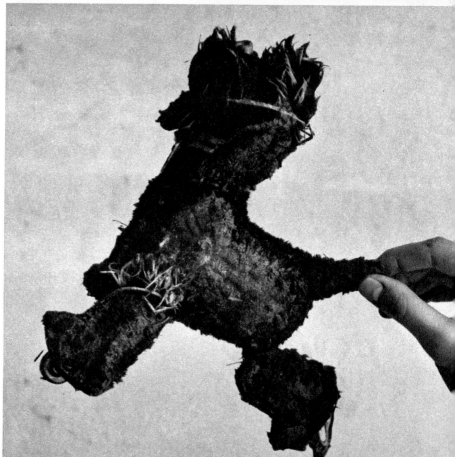

took up position at right angles to the dog. As Vauka was inspecting it with his trunk the toy dog moved its legs and hopped about. The elephant retreated and trumpeted — but it was a different kind of trumpet from the feeble squeak which the elephant gave out when confronted with the mouse. Vauka's ears were now spread widely and fanning to and fro; his trunk flew up, the tip feeling towards the temporal gland — an infallible sign that something was going to happen short= ly. He raised his head so that the tusks stood high and threatening, the tip of his trunk still resting on the temporal gland. Was this the way Vauka asked himself if he had sufficient courage to attack? (In elephants the secretions from the tem= poral gland appear to function as a stimulus.)

Then Vauka attacked. He strode towards the dog with his giant ears spread as though he wanted to cover the dog with them. Any moment now he would trample the dog underfoot. Now? But he walked by. A gust of wind blew through my hair and I just had time to duck. Vauka's trunk had just taken a swipe above my head. Had I suddenly become the target for his attack? He came on again, turned round and, walking backwards, he stormed up to the cloth dog. But once again he passed it by. Shortly before he reached the fence he swung round on his hind=quarters and gave another swipe with his trunk. Was this intended for me? So far nothing had happened to the toy dog, it still stood on the ground like a tin soldier. Could it be that Vauka associated me with the upset of the last few hours? There was a shout: "Mind your head." Another blow from the elephant's trunk. It was distinctly unpleasant, and impossible to take photographs in such circumstances. The angry elephant attacked five times and on each occasion he by= passed the dog. Suddenly, the attacks ended and everything went quiet.

The genial Vauka came strolling towards me. I wondered what he was up to. With the dog in his line of vision he came to a halt. He ignored me but clouted the dog with a single well=aimed, effortless swipe of his trunk. The dog fell over. A second swipe and the dog fell under the sole of Vauka's right foot. The massive grey column ground down like a pestle and there was a crack. It was wonderfully precise work. Then, with a little push, the right foot shoved the flattened dog towards the left foot; there was another splintering crack and the toy dog was "dead". Vauka lifted his foot, freed his victim, sniffed it and then, seizing it with his trunk, flung the shattered remnants across the paddock. So ended the cloth poodle.

The dog's legs were two inches long. Has this any significance? Is this the point at which the elephant has the courage to deal with a small animal?

A confused elephant: an elephant undoubtedly expresses embarrassment by "fingering" with the tip of his trunk. He either holds on to the edge of his ear, or fingers uncertainly around the tips of his tusks.

I have given a lot of thought to whether Vauka's attacks were aimed at me or at the dog. I have also discussed it with experts and I have come to the con= clusion that all the attacks were really aimed at the toy poodle. Elephants in the wild also make intimidating feint attacks and this is what must have happened in my experiment.

CHAPTER 14

"This Is the Police Speaking..."

SNOW DOES NOT usually come to Europe in any great quantity before Christ=
mas but one year there was a thick white carpet stretching right across Central
Europe by the third week in December. Falls were heavy and the wind blew the
snow into drifts, piling it up into corners and changing the lie of the land. Winter
had come early to the Krontal on the southern slopes of the Taunus and the land=
scape was a white wilderness. With the temperature at 16 °C. below zero nothing
stirred outside in the Kronberg Reserve, when, at six o'clock on the first day of
the holiday, the telephone bell rang insistently in the Curator's house. At this
hour Dr Georg von Opel was usually out on his early morning walk and he was
already awake even if not fully alert. He picked up the receiver and an unknown
voice said:

"Is that the Animal Reserve? I must speak to the Manager, it's very important."

"I'm afraid he's still asleep. This is von Opel speaking, can I help you?" He
listened, still only half awake and not paying a great deal of attention. "What's
the matter ... what did you say, what is at the bus stop?"

The voice at the other end patiently explained that it was the police station at
Mammolshain ringing with the information that there was a large elephant walk=
ing about at the bus station in the town. The Curator was on the alert instantly.
It could be one of the elephants from the Reserve. "Please tell your men not to
shoot, it's not dangerous or bad=tempered. Don't let them make any hasty move=
ment, just leave it alone. We'll come straight away, so don't let them shoot,
whatever you do."

The alarm was immediately given and everyone roused. Von Opel seized his
heavy elephant rifle from the weapon cupboard and loaded it just in case it should
be necessary. One never knew with elephants. Otto Dohse was ready and the
engines of the vehicles were already warming up when the elephant keeper, a
Russian named Schorsch, came running up the slope the way that Vauka had
made off over the snow. Dohse held open the door for him, told him to jump in,
and the column set off.

It is two and a half miles over the hills and through the forests, as the crow
flies, from the Reserve to Mammolshain, but the vehicles had to take the long
way round on icy roads. By the time they reached the town the streets were still
empty of people but there was no sign of Vauka. Eventually an early riser came

along and, when von Opel asked him if by any chance he had seen an elephant, he opened his eyes very wide and stared at von Opel as though he were a lunatic. He replied rather nervously but very politely that he was sorry he had not seen an elephant and then beat a hasty retreat.

The big game hunters continued to stalk their prey in the wintry setting of the town streets. The elephant was not at the bus station, but had left footprints in the snow and also a "visiting card". The large ball of dung indicated that Vauka could not be far away. They continued to tour the side streets and suddenly as they rounded a corner they saw Vauka just in front of them. He was sweeping the snow playfully off the parked cars and then, leaning his hind=quarters on the back of a Volkswagen, he bounced it up and down several times. It was all great fun as far as Vauka was concerned.

Approaching cautiously, Herr Dohse spoke to the elephant: "Come on now, Vauka, what do you think you're doing here." He had known Vauka for eight years and he scratched the tip of his trunk gently. In reply the elephant gave a little cry of recognition. "Come along, Vauka, you can't stay here," he said and three men from the Reserve encouraged the animal back to the main street. All went well for two hundred yards but by now the main street was bustling with activity. Vauka strained to get away. The police arrived and put out a general warn= ing: "Elephant loose in Mammolshain", and the situation began to look ugly. Vauka was apparently intent on finding the way back along the route by which he had come. A six=foot high garden fence blocked his way but he removed this with elephantine ease and walked in across the churchyard. It was some time before the men eventually got him back on to the main road. Then a bus full of people approached. The driver went very slowly and astonished faces peered out of the windows as Vauka came to a halt, put back his ears and trumpeted. The elephant's eye was level with the bus driver and Vauka surveyed the situation. He started to finger the driver's half=open window with his trunk. Terrified, the bus driver hastily wound up his window. But Vauka had already moved on and disappeared down a side street which led to the forest.

The tracks of the elephant and his escort ploughed deep into the snow as they trudged up the hill in the direction of Kronberg. In the meantime the telephone at the Reserve had never stopped ringing as one person after another rang to report having seen an elephant. Many of them were incoherent. They had gone out for a holiday walk expecting to enjoy the fairytale scenery in the snow and suddenly they had been confronted by an African elephant apparently wandering about the countryside entirely on its own. Herr Dohse's wife had been kept busy answering the telephone, and when someone from the café in the forest announced that there was an elephant at the front door, trying to get in and what should they do — and then hung up before she had time to answer, she wondered if anything really had happened this time.

But it all turned out right in the end. The police and the men from the Reserve caught up with Vauka at the café and with a little patience, a few kind words and some sugar=beet persuaded Vauka to go on his way again quite quietly. The elephant was now tired, he had lost all his ambition, and he willingly went ahead of his escort, back up the hill through the forest and so to the Reserve. He must have set out shortly after midnight, according to the time it took to get him home from Mammolshain, since the first news of his arrival in town had been at six in the morning.

The swing door to the den enabled him to come and go as he pleased within his paddock, and the thick snow had been blown by the wind into a drift against the fence, making it easy for the elephant to step over the fence and reach the outside world. Since the Kronberg elephants were accustomed to hard winters and indeed liked the snow, Vauka came to no harm through his escapade. He did not catch cold or develop pneumonia. In fact his prolonged walk resulted only in some muscular pain in his legs. And it was a rather stiff Vauka who strutted through the open gate to be received with joyful trumpetings by Conti and Opeline.

Two days later workmen welded tall spikes on to the upper part of the fence so that, however deep the snow, the elephants could not get out. This put an end to any further ideas of escape which Vauka and his companions might have been considering. One does not like to have elephants which escape, even when they are subsequently praised for model behaviour during their peregrinations. Even the quietest elephant can turn in the twinkling of an eye into an animal running berserk if it sees something strange when it is on unfamiliar ground. Elephants are timid by nature. They may take fright at something they see or they may equally well be startled by something they hear. There is nothing new about this, it has been recognized ever since man started to deal with elephants.

Some years ago Elia Kazan shot his Hollywood film called *Man on a Tightrope* on location in the romantic valley of the Upper Isar. The script was based on the story of the circus which made such a dramatic escape through the Iron Cur= tain in 1951, and which hit the headlines. Elia Kazan wanted to reconstruct the flight and so he engaged the heroes of the original story — the entire company of the Brumbach Circus complete with man, mouse and elephants. There was a lot of shooting in the most important sequence in the film and for weeks the elephants and the horses were rehearsed so that there was no risk of a stampede. Every day people fired pistols close to the animals so that they would become accustomed to the noise. After only one day of this the Indian elephant Jenny wrenched her chain from the floorboards of her quarters during the night and disappeared under cover of darkness into the Bavarian mountains. Next morning a sleepy stable lad rubbed his eyes when he saw the empty stable and then raised the alarm. But Gustav Brumbach had already received some information about Jenny: the head forester of Fall had just arrived with some of his men, still show= ing signs of shock and gesticulating over their shoulders: "There's a devil loose, up there — we've seen it. It's enormous and grey and it's only got one horn . . ." The forestry workers had never seen an elephant before and, as they went up to the high forest, climbing in the dim morning light, they met Jenny in person.

It is not surprising that they took to their heels and ran, arriving breathless at the head forester's house.

The wildest rumours concerning Jenny's deeds circulated throughout Isartal and, as the stories were passed from one farm to another, the jokes which Jenny played became grotesquely exaggerated. Near Fall she had met the postman doing his rounds on a bicycle. He had fallen off out of sheer fright and crawled away on all fours, while Jenny had quietly given the bicycle a new shape and then sorted out the mail which was strewn around. At one of the farms she was ap= parently not satisfied with the way in which the washing had been hung up to dry. She therefore dismantled the line noisily and then, fingering the farmer's white pants with her trunk, she disappeared into the forest waving them like a banner.

A capture squad was perpetually on her track but Jenny knew just how to elude it. On one occasion the men watched her walk along a narrow wooden bridge which had been closed as unsafe to pedestrians. The bridge creaked and groaned under the weight of Jenny's sixty=five hundredweight. In Zuckeltrab she vanished on the opposite side of the valley from her pursuers. Another time she climbed up a steep and exposed ridge in the direction of Walchensee and, having reached the top, sat down on her behind and tobogganed down a steep gravel slope on the other side. They finally caught up with her at night and encircled her. By then she was tired after her wanderings and was ready to give in. She meekly followed her keepers back into the Isar valley, ears drooping and feet very sore. They hurt so much that she picked up first one foot then another, restlessly shift= ing her weight as the men from Fall and the forestry workers stood in front of her, gazing in awe at the grey monster.

At noon the alarm was raised again. Jenny had disappeared. Owing to the carelessness of one of the stable boys she had once more managed to get free of her chain. This time she was seen heading in the direction of the River Isar. She waded out into the middle of the river and remained there, stamping up and down, trampling the water constantly and apparently relieving the smarting soreness of the soles of her feet. However, half an hour later she came trotting back behind her keeper, as docile as a dog at heel. All she had wanted was to cool her burning feet. She did not have to plan any more escapes because an understanding doctor ordered her footbaths — twice a day — in the River Isar.

CHAPTER 15

The Language of Ears and Trunks

IT IS MUCH more difficult to make a valid contribution to our knowledge about the behaviour of anthropoid apes or elephants than it is to make definite state= ments about fleas and lice. We have more precise information about cockchafers and rats than we have about giraffes and rhinoceroses. People who are not zoolo= gists — and they are always in the majority — find this astonishing and wonder why it should be. The layman assumes that it is due to chance but in fact this is not so.

Ethology, or the study of animal behaviour, which pays particular attention to behaviour in the wild, is faced with special difficulties in the case of the higher mammals. With elephants, for example, the immense technical problems would become almost insuperable if research were carried out in the animals' natural habitat. One would have to go where the herd went and be right amongst the elephants. By contrast, life is much simpler for the zoologist who is studying a small animal which can be brought into a laboratory. As a laboratory animal it can be kept under constant observation quite conveniently and for the most part the entire field of its activity kept in view.

But for the zoologist who wants to find out more about the large mammals, is there not perhaps a special fascination in trying to overcome all the difficulties which hinder his work? One who could not resist the challenge was a young zoolo= gist from the Max Planck Institute for Behaviour Physiology named Wolfdieter Kühme. When he switched from working on fish to elephants, he was well aware of the problems he would face.

He summarized under four headings what he thought would be the main diffi= culties in studying and analysing the behaviour of the largest living land mammal. First, the tendency of man to interpret the behaviour of higher mammals in a purely subjective way. Secondly, there is always the possibility, in higher mam= mals, of motivation more complex than is at first assumed. Thirdly, animals under observation can change their behaviour significantly through learning; finally, the sense organs of the animals are often better than those of the human observer. There is, therefore, much scope for errors which could lead to gross misinterpret= ation. It is hardly surprising that the layman has so many false ideas about the larger mammals.

Animals used in zoological research are mostly small in size. The classical ani=

mals for behaviour research, for instance, are fish and birds, which mainly orien=
tate by sight. Wolfdieter Kühme found the three elephants at Kronberg ideal sub=
jects for research and he wrote about them with enthusiasm:

As far as I am concerned, there is no better place for doing zoo research than
in the open Reserve of the Taunus. Two thirds of the meadow and wooded slopes
of the elephant enclosure adjoin the Königsteiner forest and the other side is
bordered by park and woodland tracks. Anyone walking out of the forest has
an uninterrupted view of three elephants in a meadow. They look unusually
small in their surroundings. In an ordinary zoo, visitors usually stand directly
in front of the elephants, which tower above them and may easily give the
impression of being rather dim=witted. In the Reserve, one gets a completely
different impression. As soon as the elephant sees a stranger near the railings it
is on the alert and it comes appreciably nearer. It does not make a direct
approach but, with head raised and ears forward, it turns its head from side
to side as though staring first with one eye and then the other. It then comes
over quickly, but even so, it still looks much smaller than a zoo elephant as it
stands under the tall trees with plenty of space around it.

It is in the solitude of the summer nights that the impact of the wild animal,
uninfluenced by man, is at its strongest. The darkness distorts the sensory im=
pressions and turns animal observation into an exciting sport: pale grey
shadows glide silently across the meadows and there are resonant rumblings
as the elephants keep in touch with one another. Suddenly a muffled sound of
bodies bumping and the harsh grating of dry skins chafing against each other
indicate that a nocturnal fight has begun. As soon as the elephants get the scent
of the human watcher, lying prone on the ground beyond the railings, they
stand stock still and then flap their ears; the proximity of a human is provoc=
ative and usually the senior bull hurries over and throws his trunk repeatedly
in the direction of the night watcher. Unable to get his forefeet over the high
fence, he fishes with his trunk, picks up a stick, whacks it against his body and
then flings it at the intruder. Elephants do not appreciate being disturbed at
night and they lay siege in no uncertain manner. There is no peace if the
human does not move off.

Dr Kühme watched the three African elephants for 180 hours spread over four=
teen days and ten nights. He often slept out in the open only fifty yards away from
them. His aim was to collect basic data, by means of constant observation, about
the behaviour of African elephants. He was particularly interested in two aspects
of behaviour. He made an intensive study of their heads and came to recognize
readily certain unmistakable expression movements. This inevitably led him to
observe what happened when elephants meet each other and to note details about
the whole body as distinct from the head, and to study the language of elephants.
Lying in the grass near the animals, the young zoologist began to note down the
vocabulary of the elephants and to lay the foundations of a "dictionary" which
would help humans to understand these giant mammals clearly.

Zoologists now use the term "display" to refer to an animal's behaviour when, as in posturing, calling, etc., it is evident that the biological significance of the behaviour lies in its special function of communicating information to other individuals. Facial expressions are such special types of behaviour, not only in elephants, but in humans, too, of course. By revealing the state of mind of one individual an expression can influence or control the behaviour of another.

Dr Kühme and I talked of elephants and exchanged experiences as we sat in his room at the Max Planck Institute at Seewiesen. I wished I had known of his work before I went on my African tour. The knowledge he had gained from his observations in the Kronberg Reserve would have been invaluable to me. I would have noticed much more and also used my camera quite differently, to far greater purpose. I was made to realize once again how important it is to study the animals available to us in captivity and to do so in detail. I consoled myself with the thought that I was not a zoologist. There is no doubt that animals in captivity frequently behave in ways which are conditioned by their captivity but the basis of their behaviour is not always affected. A behaviour study which compared observations made in the wild with those of captive animals would establish whatever differences exist and be of great interest.

While I was at Seewiesen Dr Kühme read out to me the first entry in his elephant vocabulary. When an elephant turns to attack a man, it pauses for a moment with its head raised, spreads its ears wide and walks briskly towards him with trunk hanging down. The trunk swings with greater intensity the nearer the elephant comes; when it is ten to fifteen yards from the man, its trunk forms a loop upwards and inwards. Then, when it is immediately in front of the "enemy", the tip of the trunk touches the left or right side of the head and, shortly before the actual blow with the trunk, it touches a gland in the temple. The more keen the elephant is to attack, the stiffer it holds its trunk. The Kronberg elephants delivered blows with the trunk striking upwards from below and also from the side. This is an example of a frontal attack. The attack may, however, be delivered in another way: the elephants advance on the "enemy" with ears swinging, as though intending to deliver a blow with their trunks, but they soon turn round and back on to the "enemy"; with heads raised and looking to the rear, they attempt to tread on the "enemy" with their hind feet. Sometimes they do a quick turn on their hind legs and make a horizontal stroke with the trunk stretched well out in front. This is an elephant attack from the rear.

CHAPTER 16

The Confused Elephant

AN ELEPHANT SAYS almost everything with its ears and trunk. The movements of the trunk may be compared with the nervous movements of a man's hand; they express the elephant's mood and reflect his attitude.

In all situations that excite it, an elephant spreads its ears, either markedly or to a lesser degree, so that they stand out from the body. It is only when flight is uppermost in its mind that its ears remain flat against the body. The position of the ears also gives emphasis to certain forward movements and they are held out as wide as possible in an attack.

The ears are held in an intermediate position, neither fully spread nor folded back, when the elephant is uncertain how to act. The position of the ears together with the movements of the trunk are key indicators of its mood. For instance: when the head is elevated, the ears spread out, the trunk relaxed and hanging loosely with the tip slightly curved up and forward, this means, in effect: "Watch it, here I come!" — in other words the elephant is about to attack. On the other hand, if the elephant happens to be an exceptionally wary animal, it may have reached the conclusion: "What's the point? I think I would rather retreat." In this case the head is still held high but the tip of the trunk is curved in and backwards, and the ears are flat against the body, indicating flight rather than attack.

When an elephant appears to be questioning itself the trunk touches the tem=poral glands. It is as though the animal is seeking information about itself: "Am I feeling brave enough or would it be better to retreat?" After touching the tem=poral gland, action of one kind or another may follow suddenly. There may be direct action such as a blow from the trunk, or the energy may be channelled into what is often known as displacement activity. In the latter the trunk glides from the temporal gland into the ear, where it fingers a little, and then moves over to the edge of the ear or to the forehead, and it may even touch the tusks. After this the trunk rolls up inwards or is even stuck in the mouth. The huge grey beast stands there self=consciously, very much at odds with itself, looking rather like a child sucking its finger and wondering what to do. Uncertain whether to attack or retreat and driven by these conflicting urges, the elephant seizes any con=venient object, such as food or sand for dust=baths, and either hurls the object or beats it emphatically against its own body. It will hurl branches or bits of roots at a human "enemy", aiming either backwards over its body or forwards, with a degree of violence varying according to the vehemence of its attack.

At one time when Vauka was the senior bull he developed a bad habit which was conditioned by captivity. He reacted on such occasions in the following way: he would stroll along, mostly with his back to the man, apparently taking no notice of him, and he would sweep his trunk around and along the ground — going through the same motions with his trunk as when plucking grass; he would then turn round suddenly, taking the man unawares, and chuck sand or stones in his face with uncanny precision before the man had time to dodge. On one occasion Vauka chose me as his target: the grit nearly broke my sunglasses and I was spat= tered with mud. I was so infuriated by this display of malice that I replied in like manner. I collected a handful of stones and sand and threw it at Vauka's face. This was the first time such a thing had happened to him. After that I had only to bend down when I suspected him of having any wicked ideas.

I am grateful to Dr Kühme for having given me a glimpse into the language of elephants. When I see two elephants together nowadays, I can tell which of the two holds the senior rank. Both use their trunks to touch each other's head but when it comes to the right to initiate the ceremony of mouth examining, the alpha animal has priority and it takes the direct route into the mouth of the animal opposite, going straight in under its trunk; if the lower ranking animal wishes to make the appropriate reply it has no option but to place its trunk above that of the other, in order to reach the mouth of the senior animal from the side. It is also the alpha animal's exclusive right to feel for the temporal gland of the lower ranking animal; the latter is expected to reply by touching the ear of the senior animal. If the lower ranking animal fails to react to the address and does not make the appropriate response, the alpha animal gets annoyed and at once be= comes aggressive. This is because it affects his status as leader of the group. Every time a lower ranking animal responds correctly to the touch of the senior, the latter's social position is re=affirmed. This may be done hundreds of times during a single day.

CHAPTER 17

The Reform of an Irresponsible Father

SHE HAD TAKEN so much trouble. She had tried everything but it had all been in vain and she could not understand why. It had all started when a fine=looking male with a deep bass voice came to court her. There was a vibrant booming sound as he approached. Then he ran very fast, rushing over the ground to get to her as quickly as possible and, with his wings held stiffly away from his body, his long feathers quivering, he strutted around her. During this display he managed to look both dignified and elegant in spite of his rather clumsy feet. She found him irresistible and he took her home with him.

All that was a little while ago and having made a beautiful depression in the ground for her he had taken his leave. Today she was on her own. She had been deserted and she could not understand why. She had done everything she should have done. She had laid him a large egg every second day. She could not lay any faster because it takes time to produce an egg weighing over a quarter of a pound. It took her nearly two weeks to lay six eggs. This number should have been sufficient to make him think about his parental duties, because, according to the rhea code of behaviour, it is the father's duty to incubate and rear the young. To make quite sure, she laid him another eight eggs and then she gave up. He did not even look at the nest; in fact, for the past four weeks he had been keeping another female company. Fourteen eggs now lay waiting in the nest. What would happen to them?

All this took place in the Kronberg Reserve, where animal behaviour experts were watching the outcome of this unsuccessful alliance. At this stage they decided to take a hand: eight of the big white eggs went into an incubator and it was decided to experiment with the remaining six. Two broody turkey=hens were required and these were produced. Three of the abandoned eggs were given to each turkey=hen and, although they must have found them uncomfortably large, the two hens accepted them without fuss and immediately began to incubate.

Every care was taken of the eggs in the incubator but none of them hatched. At first all went well with the turkey=hens but after four weeks of incubating one of them gave up and left the nest. Twenty=eight days is the normal incubation period for turkeys and after this the eggs should hatch. When nothing happened in her nest the turkey=hen got impatient and nothing would persuade her to remain sitting; she had every right to abdicate after twenty=eight days and so she retired from "Operation Rhea Egg". The other turkey=hen was more phlegmatic and had no objection to sitting for a longer time. From the point of view of the experiment she was a model broody hen and after thirty=five days of incubating she had her reward. All the eggs hatched and three bizarrelooking chicks imme= diately stood up on their hind legs and, turning their heads on typically long thin necks, the young rheas gazed inquisitively at the world. The turkey=hen might look dumpy compared with the stilt=legged birds but she had managed to hatch the brood. She had also done this in spite of having a far higher incubation temperature than that of a rhea. Man had intervened and sprayed the rhea eggs twice a day with tepid water; they would otherwise have dried up in the heat generated by the turkey=hen's body.

The odd=looking family group now ran about together in a small paddock. In the first few days the turkey foster=mother appeared to have some difficulty with the strange language of the chicks; she found the unfamiliar piping calls of the young South American rarities rather bewildering. But the rearing urge was now fully aroused in her and demanded satisfaction. On the other hand the rhea chicks seemed to understand instantly their foster=mother's expressions — her call= notes and alarm=notes — and after a while nothing seemed to disturb the under= standing between these two species which were so foreign to each other. The rhea chicks appeared to be "imprinted", as the animal behaviourists call it, on the turkey=hen. She did not seem to mind the shape of their bodies, nor their long= legged appearance and the long strides they took. Possibly she generously over= looked these "abnormalities" in her foster=children. She certainly reared them with touching devotion.

As they were a closely=knit group it was decided to risk releasing the turkey= hen with her charges so that they could wander about the park together amongst the other rheas, including the father who had deserted them. There was some anxiety about the cock rhea's possible reaction to them and so for the first day a man was assigned to them to act as shepherd; he followed the turkey=hen, armed with a big stick, to ward off any possible attack. In fact, nothing happened. The big rhea did not recognize these small striped birds as belonging to his species and he took no notice of them. He had not incubated eggs or reared young previously and they did not come within his range of experience.

For a time everything went well. After five weeks, however, a keeper reported that the adult male rhea had suddenly started to take an interest in the young rheas. The observers were not sure why this should suddenly happen. They noticed that the rhea circled round the turkey=hen and her chicks, which were now much larger than their foster=mother, and that the circle grew tighter. What had aroused this sudden concern for them? The turkey=hen defended her brood fiercely from the giant. It was a somewhat grotesque picture to see the large rhea being made to keep his distance by the small turkey. He behaved with decorum and did not come within the prescribed area, but from now on he was drawn more and more to the turkey=hen and her chicks. She was in a perpetual state of anxiety,

continually uttering frenzied screams in an attempt to protect herself from his persis=
tent attentions. Could it be that the rhea had suddenly adopted a parental role?

Detailed observations on the behaviour of the rhea had been noted down with
precise dates and a record of the development of the chicks had similarly been
kept. On comparing entries in both notebooks it was found that the date when
the father started paying attention to his children coincided with the start of a
colour change in the plumage of the chicks. As their new feathers gradually grew
out from the down, the plumage of the young rheas resembled that of their father
for the first time and it was then that he recognized them as belonging to his own
species. With the help of the turkey=hen, he had unintentionally become a father
and for the first time in his life his rearing urge was awakened and released. It
was quite clear to all who watched his efforts that the maternal activities of the
turkey=hen could not last much longer.

For the last two weeks the turkey=hen had looked after only two chicks. The
third had unfortunately lost its footing when dodging about and fallen in the
pond. It drowned before a keeper could rescue it, in spite of the fact that fully
grown rheas swim reasonably well and will go into the water of their own accord.

The final act in the drama took place one morning in the rain. The turkey=hen
was out in the meadow, walking and pecking at the wet grass and accompanied
by her two large children. The jealous father again set to work on the ill=assorted
trio but on this particular morning he changed his tactics. He no longer attacked
the turkey=hen but, every time she bent down to peck, he took a couple of steps
nearer to them. At a distance of perhaps six feet the cock displayed; he made
himself look very big, puffing himself out and extending his wings so that all the
feathers shook; he behaved, in fact, as though he were courting. The turkey=hen
eyed him suspiciously. A few deep notes came from his inflated throat. Then in
the wind and rain he moved in with a great swishing noise and, booming at the
young rheas, he came to a halt right in their path. The turkey=hen was unprepared
for this assault and stood stock still, as though she were paralysed. The next thing
she saw was the father rhea running off with the two children racing along behind
him. He never stopped running and it was as though the young rheas were
delighted at having found someone who could run faster than they; their foster=
mother had been unable to play this game with them. The turkey=hen still remained
motionless, looking after her fast=disappearing family. For nearly two months she
had cared for the two chicks, centering her maternal feelings on them, and now
in a few seconds they had been abducted by their father who had suddenly
remembered his parental duties. She started to call them anxiously. They heard
her in the distance but as soon as they started to follow her voice the father
rushed across to them. This happened several times during the first few days
following the abduction but after that everyone accepted the situation, which was,
after all, the normal one.

Next year the same rhea seemed to want to make up for his deficiencies of the
previous year and he became a super=father. In the spring everything went as

nature intended and, after his courtship, the hen laid the eggs in the nest. This time there were only eleven and he sat on them as though it were the most natural thing in the world. He incubated for a period of thirty=nine days. The weather was unfortunately such that only four small rheas hatched out, but he showed as much solicitude for them as the foster=mother had done the previous year. This time, however, the hen laid her second clutch much too late. Normally these are brooded at the same time as the first clutch, but suddenly nine new eggs appeared in a nest near by instead of in the same nest, as usually happens. With the best will in the world the cock rhea could not incubate and at the same time feed and look after the four chicks which had already hatched. The nine eggs were therefore taken to an incubator, where, after forty days, two chicks hatched out. The problem then was what to do with these two. Would the cock still accept them? He did, and as though this was a normal arrangement, he took charge of the two youngsters from the second brood. The juvenile plumage no longer seemed strange to him and he made up for his shortcomings of the previous year. The two broods were six weeks apart and the first batch had already shed their down when he started to rear the two age groups simultaneously.

This delightful story which the observers found so interesting could only have taken place in captivity. In their natural surroundings of the South American plains the deserted eggs of the first year would either have been taken by predators or just rotted on the ground and the second brood of the following year would also never have seen the light of day.

Nature is hard. During the next few years the augmented rhea population in the reserve was decimated owing to a combination of the weather and predation by foxes and birds of prey. An unnatural sex ratio was the result. The rhea is normally polygamous, courting five or six hens. In the abnormal circumstances of the Reserve at that time, three male rheas had to fight for the favours of a single hen and, of necessity, they courted each other. Another year, this led to a curious situation in which a male successfully courted a female, took her to the nest where she laid the requisite number of eggs and then failed to take over the incubation. Three other males noticed at once and they took turns in the incubation of the brood. Ostriches, which are closely related, also take turns, the male and the female dividing the watch at the nest between them. And the result in the case of the rheas? Not a single chick hatched out because too many cooks spoil the broth.

CHAPTER 18

Beautiful but Useless

ONE MORNING IN early spring I went to the Munich Zoo with a definite plan in mind. I intended to take colour photographs of the Greater Kudu, an African antelope with twisted horns, and of Grevy's Zebra, the zebra with the bushy ears. I needed both these photographs for a specific purpose and I went straight to the Kudu enclosure. Things did not turn out as I intended, however, and I finished up with some quite different pictures.

It was still early as the gatekeeper greeted me. The sun was only just coming up over the Siebenbrunn slope, shedding its golden light on the treetops in the park. It would not be long before its rays would melt the white hoar frost covering the ground. The Kudu run was empty. This beautiful animal was too valuable to let out on such frosty ground. From where I stood near the Elephant House I could see the Grevy's Zebras still in their den. There was nothing to do but wait and so I sat down on a bench under a huge willow tree with my cameras already loaded beside me. Suddenly there was a plop near me, then another, and the third was a direct hit. I jumped up and felt my head; a greenish=white mucilage stuck to the palm of my hand. It did not smell very pleasant and I swore. Looking up I saw the cause of it all: the whole willow tree was full of peafowl. It so happened that the bench was situated right under their roosting place. One of their salvoes had landed right on my Rolleiflex and it was essential to have a good clean=up; first the camera, then my head. This may not have seemed a very good start to the morning but it turned out to be a stroke of good luck.

Just as I finished cleaning the viewfinder there was the most extraordinary noise above me. The whole company in the tree were shifting around and the noise I could hear was made by the long quills of the male birds as the shafts of the feathers in their fan=shaped tails rubbed against each other. I counted twenty=one birds in the branches of the old willow, a most unusual sight, making me forget all about the guano on my head. Fortunately the leaves were not out on the willow and I could see them all clearly; another two weeks and they would have been screened completely by a curtain of greenery.

The sun mounted higher and a pair which had been sunning themselves for some time in the crown of the tree were the first to start preening. Others which had roosted in the lower branches started to stretch, shaking the stiffness from

Rheas feeding. These South American relatives of the ostrich have settled down well in our latitudes. They are hardy and undemanding in captivity. Their breeding, however, brings some surprises because the male incubates and rears the young.

Above: a brooding male rhea. The female lays the eggs in a shallow depression scratched out by the male, who incubates the eggs for 35 to 40 days.

Right: what happens when the male refuses to accept the eggs laid in his nest? On one occasion when the staff of the Kronberg Reserve were faced with this problem they solved it by putting the large rhea eggs under a broody turkey. Three long=legged chicks hatched and in spite of some "language difficulties" the turkey=hen reared and cared for them as though they were her own. After a short while the young rheas outgrew their foster=mother and exchanged their longitudi= nally striped feathers for the typical rhea plumage.

The father rhea showed an increasing interest in them as they grew. As long as they retained their juvenile plumage he failed to recognize them as his own species but as they assumed the distinctive rhea plumage he became increasingly energetic in his attempts at approaching them. They were in fact his first brood and because he failed to incubate them he had not experienced their hatching. For weeks the small turkey, driven by maternal instinct, defended them from the growing attentions of the father rhea, showing both skill and courage. Then one morning he succeeded in driving the chicks in front of him by raising his wings so that the long feathers trailed in the wind while he boomed loudly at them. The turkey=hen was taken completely by surprise and merely stood stock=still as he abducted the young rheas.

Young rheas have a comical appearance and they look like something out of a child's picture book.

A rhea father with his clutch of eggs. He looks after his offspring with the devotion of a mother.

It is only when the willow is leafless that one can see the peafowl's sleeping quarters high up in the tree. The birds fly out of the willow to their courtship grounds. Four peacocks launched them= selves from the tree all at the same time. They passed overhead "on angels' wings, with the tread of an assassin and the voice of the devil", as the Romans described them.

When the courtship display has finished the cocks become more tolerant of one another's presence and they gather in small groups with the grey=brown hens. There may be some bickering between quarrelsome males but no chase such as that on the courtship ground takes place.

Left: the peacock attracts the peahen simply by spreading his tail. This ritual announces his presence to distant females who approach at the signal. It is the female who selects the male. If she pecks the ground in front of him, as though picking up grain, this indicates that she is watching his display; he then rustles his long tail=coverts with golden=blue "eyes" and stamps his spurred feet on the ground.

their feathers after the cold night as the sun crept down the tree. The uppermost peacock had already half spread his tail and he was the first to extend it fully; the others followed suit as the warmth reached them lower down. The scene should really have been filmed. It was as though the willow tree gradually unfolded from the top, spreading out into a huge iridescent flower of blue, green and gold in the bare branches. I need scarcely say that the lords of the peafowl world take a great deal longer over their morning toilet than the ladies. The peahen with her shorter dress always finishes first. The peacocks devote much more time to their magnifi= cent trains, which are easily a yard long.

The peahens soon flew away, leaving only the males completing their toilet in the willow tree. Hastily they went on with their preening – after all, the first one to reach the mating ground gets the best chance. They became rather agitated, hop= ping about in the branches, making for the jumping off place in the tree. This consisted of some special branches looking out over the park.

There was a rush of air and a whirring sound as the first peacock took off. It sailed over my head silhouetted against the bright=blue sky. The powerful prima= ries and the tail feathers glistened white overhead and even in the air the tail feathers appeared to be holding up the long, coloured tail=coverts which form the peacock's fan. I had never seen peacocks flying like this before, standing directly below their line of flight. First one shot out of the tree, then another, then a mass in quick succession. The willow tree was almost empty and only four remained, still hopping about in the branches looking for a suitable launching site. Suddenly they all took off together, as though at a starter's gun: four peacocks in the air making an improbable picture in blue, white and various browns – it was a fab= ulous sight accompanied by the rustle of a thousand feathers. Their spurred feet were held in a convulsive clutch as though they expected merely to leap from one branch to another, contradicting all the rules of streamlining in which the under= carriage is retracted to avoid wind resistance. But they looked proud of themselves and as though they were quite accustomed to flying about – supremely elegant but with a hint of violence in the menacing positioning of the claws.

The peacocks did not cover much ground in their gliding flight, they merely sailed over the expanse between the willow tree and the bank of the stream, a dis= tance of about two hundred yards. They did not follow the peahens but made straight for their mating ground, which was in another direction. The cocks are much too beautiful to have to chase after their mates. Each of them has a favour= ite mating area which is trodden as flat as possible; here the male does nothing but stand and display his richly coloured tail, a signal which can be seen from a long way off. The hens come over and watch the invitation display because it is

The tail=coverts fan out to reveal a mass of iridescence marked with blue=brown=gold "eyes". There are often more than 160 "eyes". The iridescence is produced by the break=up of light by ultra= thin, colourless lamellae in the feathers, each one a fraction of one thousandth of a millimetre thick.

the females who choose the males. If the female stands in front of the male and pecks, it indicates that she is aware of his invitation. Then he rattles his long tail= coverts with the golden=blue "eyes", stamps his spurred feet and, with a sideways towing action of his wings, turns round on his own axis, presenting his rear to the hen, which she finds no less interesting. He rattles his plumage again and lowers his white wing feathers until they graze along the ground. Finally he turns round and finds her waiting for him, already sitting on the ground.

After pairing has taken place she goes right away and makes a nest somewhere on the ground, re=appearing four weeks later with a brood of attractive chicks. Peafowls are tree=dwellers and the hen sleeps on the ground only for the first few nights after the chicks have hatched. As soon as they are fully mobile she jumps up with them into the lower branches of the bushes.

Peafowl have been kept in captivity for 2,000 years. They originate from the jungle forests of southern Asia, and it was Alexander the Great who brought the first peacock from India with him. These exotic animals quickly acclimatized them= selves to the hard climate of our latitudes. They stay out in the most severe win= ters in the Munich Zoo, keeping in good condition in spite of the cold. They remain faithful to their roosting tree even when they wake up frozen and covered with hoar frost.

The peacock is useless except for its ornamental beauty. It does not grow attached to humans, never becoming really tame. It serves no gastronomic purpose since its flesh is as tough as shoe leather. It is not even a good watch=dog, as many people claim, hoping to find an excuse for its hideous screams. It was only on account of its fabulous beauty that Alexander the Great threatened anyone who slew a peacock with the death penalty. The peacock can, therefore, claim to be the object of the first animal protection law.

In spite of all this it has become a widespread domestic animal — a bird "with the feathers of an angel, the step of an assassin and the voice of the devil", as the ancient Romans so aptly described it.

CHAPTER 19

Hermann Takes Pride of Place

A COMMUNITY OF sacred or Hamadryas baboons lived in a large meadow below a rock cliff. On the first warm day of the year the scene was tranquil with the baboons sitting in the sunshine, grooming and sunning themselves in the meadow. From time to time the peace was shattered by outbursts of high=pitched screams which came from some of the females. As far as one could see nothing out of the ordinary had occurred to give rise to this alarm. One middle=aged group, for instance, sat quietly together as though they were enjoying some feminine gossip. One was nearly bald, the second had a cough and the third was srcof= ulous. All three suddenly screamed for no apparent reason, jumped apart and looked round anxiously as they fled. A similar commotion started in another corner amongst some young females. Were they all becoming hysterical? Apart from these spasmodic outbursts the scene was quite peaceful.

A handsome young male, nicknamed Haila, came swaggering along to inspect the groups, which were busily engaged in grooming. He covered the ground with swinging strides, using his arms as forelegs, spreading them wide and swaying slightly as he balanced. It was obvious that he was feeling rather a fine fellow on this spring morning. A party of young baboons chattered and screamed with ex= citement as they rushed headlong in a boisterous game of tag, surrounding the handsome young male and jostling him unintentionally in the excitement of the game. They hastily crouched down and, still screaming hideously, presented their hindquarters to Haila; holding their tails stiffly erect, they expressed humble apo= logies for having offended him. Crouching low they cast anxious glances up at the object of their reverence but Haila was otherwise engaged. He stopped and surveyed the situation. Over to his left three maidens were grooming, squatting close to one another. He looked them over slowly and then raised his eyebrows — once, twice, three times — and three times more. He eyed them keenly. The females grew restless, squinting up at him from lowered heads for a fraction of a second and then, screaming loudly, they scattered. The handsome young Haila had done nothing but just look at them. There was something in the air on this warm spring day. The three fugitives joined up again and sat down in the imme= diate vicinity of a powerful male known as Hermann. He was in the prime of life. He leaned back against the rock cliff and raised one arm indolently in the air.

Immediately one of the three females hopped up to him and started parting the hair on his upper arm with her long pointed fingers. Then Hermann opened his large mouth and gave a huge yawn, revealing his canines. Four snow=white teeth — two up and two down — flashed dangerously from his pink gums. The canines of a male baboon are his weapons and the terror of all leopards. Hermann's yawn was a threat because the three females were members of his harem and young Haila's amorous looks at them had not escaped his attention. He made his annoy= ance known. Haila saw the threatening yawn and moved off.

The previous spring had passed unnoticed by Haila but now that he was twelve months older he had the feeling all at once that he wanted to make his presence felt. He had been on the move for several days, gazing at the prospect and spoiling for fights. He sought out baboons of his own age and after a brawl he regularly emerged as the victor, often with his fur torn and bleeding from his wounds. His self=confidence had increased recently with the growth of a thick grey cape, the distinguishing mark of the adult male sacred baboon. None of Haila's contempo= raries now dared to dispute his strength and he was confident of his position as the third=strongest male in the community. Hermann was the overlord of the first group and Otto was master of the second group. Haila was the next strongest male on the hill but as yet he had no followers. Everyone recognized that the time had now come for Haila to form his own group and this was the cause of the unrest. As he wandered through the community, issuing his challenge and flaunt= ing his strength, the females tried to get out of his way as quickly as possible.

A few years ago Haila had seen how Otto had fought to establish his group. At that time Otto had wooed Haila's mother most passionately although Haila's sec= ond brother — a son of Hermann, like Haila — was only three months old and still clinging to her belly. This had not deterred Otto in the slightest. On the contrary, a desirable female with child would be a most successful way of augmenting his group. The only drawback was that the coveted female still belonged to Hermann, who held her very firmly. She was, in fact, one of his most beautiful wives and as is customary he kept his mate in order with a series of sharp nips. Otto's choice was therefore very unfortunate and he had no luck. He turned his attention next to the rest of the harem. All the females on the cliff at that time belonged to Her= mann. They had grown so numerous that with increasing age Hermann had begun to lose control and only worried about his favourites. Otto therefore started making up to the females who were low on Hermann's list. One of these was Len= chen, the female with the goitre. She had been a prime favourite of Hermann's, but time alters all things and she appeared to be particularly out of favour at this juncture; and so Otto tried his luck with the rape of Lenchen. This resulted in a minor quarrel between the two males, but it was more in the nature of a formal protest and no blood was shed as Hermann relinquished his lowest grade female to Otto. Afterwards Otto had repeated this strategy every now and again, build= ing his harem from the lowest upwards, so to speak, taking a female when she was momentarily out of favour.

Haila was now faced with the problem of acquiring some females, all of which already belonged either to Otto or Hermann. Both of them kept a watchful eye on the younger male strutting about and parading to impress the community. Haila stole an occasional glance at the two males on the cliff and it was unmistakably clear that he could not expect to gain possession of a female without a fight.

At six years of age Haila became aware of something which must have been right under his nose all the time: Otto's females were not as exciting or as desir= able as those belonging to Hermann. Like all males, Haila yearned for desirable females and in consequence he could not take his eyes off Hermann's harem. There was one in particular: Siri, a well=proportioned female, had bewitched him and he had the impression that she was not entirely unaware of him. Haila came nearer with measured strides, Siri was certainly aware of him now. . . . The next thing he knew — and he never saw it happen — was that Hermann was already on top of him. Uproar broke out on the cliff. Hundreds of voices uttered a double note, a rapid barking sound, and rising above it all was the hoarse high=pitched voice of Hermann, the overlord of the cliff. The whole community was in an uproar as the two males fought. Shrill falsetto voices screamed and barked in support. Mothers seized their children and fled from the vicinity of the fight. The favourite females ran screaming amongst one another. Was their fate being decided? Would there be a new leader on the cliff? It was just as well that the more vulnerable parts of the males were covered by thick, silver=grey mantles or the fight would have been disastrous for both of them. Hermann's fangs sank deep into Haila's pelt but the young male reacted promptly, drawing blood in return. This infuriated Hermann, who still saw himself as the strongest baboon on the cliff, and he set about giving Haila a beating which he would remember all his life. The fact that it was father fighting son was totally irrelevant.

Soon it was all over, both the wife=stealing and the fight. But Siri gave a long look out of the corner of her eye at the retreating figure of Haila.

Haila's wounds were very painful. They impeded his movements and he had a bad limp. But nature had endowed the quarrelsome baboon with a very healthy skin and Haila was able to walk normally again after a few days. His external wounds all healed remarkably quickly and easily. The hurt to his pride was much more severe, however. He picked the scabs from his wounds. It might have been better to steal one of Otto's mates. He was nothing like as strong as Hermann and it would be well worth looking at his females in greater detail. There might be a chance later on to take the beautiful Siri from Hermann.

When Haila went to look at Otto's harem he found the three best females groom= ing the fur and skin of their lord and master. Should he attempt to steal one of these? Otto would certainly react in the same way as Hermann, and Haila did not feel strong enough yet to face a similar drama. He looked around. A trio of Otto's other females were sitting to one side. These three occupied a lower place in the hierarchy and originated from the days when Otto founded his harem. They were certainly no longer fresh or beautiful. There was the goitrous Lenchen — who had been Hermann's favourite mate at one time — and there was the bald Lotte and the coughing Biene. For some time they had been living a little apart because they were not breeding. They had had to make way for younger females and Otto could no longer be very interested in them. Haila looked at them again, sizing them up. He decided to lower his sights and forget his ambitious ideas. His experience with Hermann had made him face up to reality. He would establish his first harem with three not very presentable females belonging to Otto. A week later there was a minor scuffle and then Lenchen, Lotte and Biene changed ownership and went to Haila. The third group was now established and Haila was by no means disappoint= ed with his first collection of females. They bloomed afresh with their new master. He found that females who were somewhat past their best years were capable of showing remarkable gratitude. They danced attendance on him all day long. They did not allow a speck of dust, a crumb of dirt or a spot of scaly skin to remain on him. There was one other advantage: he need have no fear that anyone would try to steal them from him. When he went for a stroll around the cliff, he was closely attended by his three females, who either marched shoulder to shoulder close alongside him or in a row behind him.

It was naturally clear to the young group leader that he and his family took third place in the general life of the community. Hermann was still the sole over= lord of the cliff and as such all the privileges were his, in accordance with the age= old code of the baboons. He had to be first at everything. Woe betide any in= habitant who took a bite at feeding time before Hermann; he would find himself receiving some painful instruction on table manners. No one was allowed to touch food until the leading baboon had something in his cheek pouches and this act had to be carried out — at least symbolically — before even the members of his own group might eat. Meanwhile the second group were forced to wait until Hermann's dependants had satisfied their hunger. Hermann kept a sharp watch and when they showed signs of having had enough, the second group approached. Haila and his family had to be content with what was left. Hermann took particular care to see that this order of precedence was observed. He yawned angrily to put a stop to any premature approach to the feeding place by Otto or Haila.

The harsh rules of priority in feeding work towards the maintenance of the species. Father eats first, mother comes next, then the young people and finally the children. This is the exact opposite of what has become customary amongst hum= ans in the western world. When the public throws food to monkeys in a zoo, one can often see either a strong male or a mother leap down to snatch the food from the youngsters. More often than not the human donor waves a stick or an umbrella in protest at the heartlessness of the adults in depriving the dear little monkeys. But it is wrong to allow human feelings to enter a situation in which animals are involved. It is basically right that the strongest male should feed first. The most powerful male baboon is also the protector of the entire family and his strength must be maintained or increased. The mothers must also be strong so that they can carry their babies when retreating from danger, leaving the male to carry on the fight as cover for the withdrawal of his family. If the leader is weak the whole group may fall an easy prey to the enemy. This is why Hermann always fed first.

Keeper Thomson, who witnessed the harem building by Otto and Haila, took me into the enclosure after telling me the history of this baboon community. My presence as a stranger in their territory was the signal for a general alarm. The whole troop barked furiously. There was no sign of any separation into families — a united party opposed me. The powerful males stood in front, apparently equal in a situation of resistance to my presence. It was a remarkable picture of unity and I would never have guessed from it that there was any rivalry between the three males. It was a curious sensation to be greeted by such unanimous hostility. The noise was frightful. As we entered the enclosure from the ditch the troop immediately retreated to its flight distance. This corresponded with the distance which I knew from experience in the wild: fifteen to twenty yards. Hermann ran along the top terrace of his fortress high above me, showing off his muscular limbs and making impressive gestures. He still avoided looking at me. If a baboon looks you directly in the eye, this is a provocative act according to the baboon ritual. Hermann obviously wanted to find out what I was doing before issuing a direct challenge. "The one sitting over there is Siri," explained the Keeper. So that was the beauty who had taken Haila's fancy. I tried to keep an eye on Hermann all the time but for a moment he was nowhere to be seen and so I took a step nearer Siri with my camera. There was a raucous bark and Hermann shot to the edge of the terrace, holding on tightly with both hands and screaming down at me. I had committed an outrage merely by entering his territory, but to approach Siri was unheard of. . . . Hermann was directly above me on the cliff and I could see his powerful teeth flashing quite clearly. Would he jump at my face? He stared directly at me, challenging me. I remembered the story of Haila's fight with him and, since I was clearly on the losing side, I stepped back. I was not particularly keen to make closer acquaintance with Hermann. Suddenly a stone came hurtling down. I looked up at the cliff. A whole group of young baboons had gathered around Siri and were kicking up a row. From below I could not see many of the baboons but every now and again a head appeared from behind a rock and rapidly disappeared again. I kept a sharp lookout because I had a feeling that the stone had come from somewhere up there. I had had a similar experience in Sinde Canyon in the Semliki in the Congo, when a whole troop of baboons had entrenched themselves in the sandstone cliffs and had flung stones at me. Why should these baboons not do so here? I caught sight of a half-grown little baboon with a big stone in his arms! He appeared to be changing his position or perhaps he was bringing up fresh ammunition. Maybe he was the rear gunner? This little chap had certainly not seen it done in the Semliki, it was in his blood; perhaps it was an innate behaviour pattern supplemented by learning.

Keeper Thomson was not quite sure of the baboons and he decided that it would be best to feed them. As soon as they saw the food I was forgotten. They began to form up and I was able to distinguish the different groups without difficulty.

Hermann had immediately abandoned his position of defence at the sight of the food and the community was once again divided into three. The baboons came running from all directions as Thomson divided up the food. They even forgot baboon protocol and started to eat. Suddenly Hermann landed in the middle of them with a huge leap. A few hoarse barks were sufficient to disperse them and they screamed as they hurried out of his way. Otto and Haila, with their families, waited behind Hermann in their customary places. Hermann took his time filling his cheek pouches. He was even annoyed by his senior wives and he scared them off with a lordly shake of the head. His preoccupation with the food lasted quite a while. When I saw the members of his family approaching, I was not aware that he had given them any signal but they must have known that he was ready, possibly by some sign invisible to the human eye. One of his favourite wives sat down with her small offspring close by her side — it was one of Hermann's many sons — and Hermann let her stay. The others moved in. Full up and quite satisfied, he withdrew. His family could now feed undisturbed. Their lord and master marched up and down, continually giving threat yawns, keeping guard over his family. Otto and Haila moved forwards, temporarily abandoning their waiting place. I could hear Hermann's group smacking their lips in front of me and everything was quite peaceful.

A dark shadow suddenly passed over me from the edge of the cliff and a riot broke out. The battle raged back and forth. I could not make out who was fighting whom, all I saw was a lot of scrapping. The animals at the food quickly dispersed, scattering in alarm. Who would dare to take such a liberty with Hermann's group? It was Otto. I did not see him until after he had been driven away and was walking back to his waiting place. It looked as though he had got tired of the others loitering over the food, afraid that there would not be enough for his family. Haila had not become involved in the trouble but had watched it all from a distance. One never knew. It was always wise to be on the alert. If Hermann should not be feeling strong the whole structure of the community could change in a flash. But on this occasion the *status quo* was maintained.

Hermann became very excited after this upset. His family appeared to be satisfied and there was no reason to hold on to the feeding place any longer. To establish the peace he took a walk around the cliff, walking very deliberately with measured strides, accompanied by his four beautiful wives, the strongest young males behind them, then all the females and the babies together. His group went on a round tour and then came back to the feeding place. When Hermann returned, Otto and his group behaved quite amiably. Otto crouched very low and made his deepest bow so that his pink behind appeared above his followers, who were still smacking

His name is Hermann and he is the overlord of all the baboons on the cliff. He and his group have privileges which are generally respected by the community. It would be wrong, for instance, for either of the other two leaders to take his group to the feeding place before Hermann's clan.

Hermann is a harsh taskmaster. All must obey his orders. He looks round severely as his greedy harem approaches; the females are already moving off in response to his command. As soon as Hermann has filled his cheek pouches he will allow his own group to feed. Meanwhile the other families must wait at a respectful distance. Once his group is satisfied, Otto's group will be allowed to move in and finally Haila with his family will be permitted to approach the food.

Left, above and below: if a stranger intrudes into the kingdom of the baboons the well=defined groups which are usually so sharply divided band together for mutual defence. Hermann, the overlord of the entire community, has ordered everyone on to the cliff. He and his bravest youngster threaten the enemy from the ramparts. Siri, his favourite wife at the time, squats beside him. A stone suddenly hurtles down from the cliff — Hermann's young guard has fired on the enemy. I caught one of the marksmen with my camera just as he was changing his position.

203

Uproar at the feeding place: Otto, the leader of the second group, got tired of waiting and gate=crashed at the feast of his superiors. In a lightning attack, Hermann flashed his dagger=like canines and Otto retreated. With his position confirmed, Hermann marches off with his family in the classical victory parade of the baboons. He leads the way, surrounded by his favourite wives, followed first by the young males, and those with young children bring up the rear.

Bottle=fed Sibyl was a little rhesus monkey who was rejected by her parents in the Heidelberg Zoo. A few hours after her birth she was rescued by her keeper, in a hand=to=hand struggle, from her enraged father, who was about to kill her. She was then adopted by humans. When she was six months old she had a terrifying experience: she was out for a walk and she saw monkeys for the first time. They were her own parents but she was terrified of them. She leaped into the arms of her human foster=father and nearly had a heart attack.

Sibyl had a deep=seated fear of monkeys. She roamed freely all round the zoo, avoiding only the monkey enclosure. Her human foster=father, Horst, was given a motor=scooter for his eighteenth birthday and a few weeks later another significant incident took place. I was sitting in front of the zoo office with Horst, and Sibyl was teasing us in true monkey fashion. Then she saw the motor=scooter in the yard and she was soon sitting in the saddle and doing gymnastics on the handle=bars. Suddenly she gave a loud scream and shot into the air: she had caught sight of her own reflection in the mirror. There had been no scent to warn her and the sight of her own monkey face staring at her gave her a horrible fright.

their lips. This gesture of submission acknowledged the presence of the others and satisfied Hermann. Both families fed quietly together. Haila and his family were forced to wait. They eventually got the left=overs.

I could now take my departure unmolested. Half an hour later the three leaders were sitting quite close to one another in the meadow at the foot of the cliff. Everything was peaceful. The next item on the day's programme was cleaning and grooming. A well=groomed appearance can only be achieved through mutual assist= ance and appearance is everything — even on monkey hill.

Horst with his adopted child Sibyl. She springs onto his shoulder whenever she can and care= fully starts giving him the monkey treatment. Skin=grooming is all=important. She is just removing some sleep matter from the corner of her keeper's eye.

CHAPTER 20

The Young Monkey Who Was Afraid of Monkeys

ONE BITTERLY COLD morning in January keeper Erich went on his first rounds through the zoological park. It was a routine inspection and Erich did not stop for long at any of the paddocks. He could tell at a glance whether everything was in order. After looking at Thusnelde, the big female camel, he went straight over to the open paddock where the monkeys were making a wild clamour. There was nothing unusual in this as monkeys are always squabbling amongst themselves, but suddenly Erich pricked up his ears: he heard a high=pitched whimpering which was not normally there. He decided to investigate in case the monkeys had caught something. He strode over to the wire=netting fence and was astonished to see Jacob, the large male rhesus, rampaging about like a madman and clutching in his left hand something that was shrieking. He dragged it along behind him and it looked like a dead, skinned rat. It shrieked again but Jacob's furious screams drowned the noise. Erich looked again very carefully. It was a newly born monkey. He realized that he had no alternative: he would have to go straight into the cage and somehow get it away from the infuriated adult.

The female rhesus Mimi must have given birth in between the keeper's rounds. It was her first mating with Jacob and apparently it had aroused no maternal feeling in her. Erich noticed that, while Jacob was rampaging around with her newly born infant, she sat in her normal place quite unconcerned. The heart=rending screams of her own baby had no effect on her whatsoever; on the contrary, it even looked as though Mimi were inciting him with sharp little cries.

Erich rushed through the paddock door, seized the broom which was leaning against it and advanced on Jacob in an effort to make him give up the infant monkey. But a strong male rhesus does not relinquish his booty as easily as this. The baby was blue with cold. Jacob had it by the tail and it was still whimpering. Erich gave chase in a determined effort to save its life. Jacob evaded him at every turn and never once let go of his prize. Finally, the keeper succeeded in cornering him and struck a severe blow with the broom handle across Jacob's shoulder. The frantic rhesus screamed and let go of the baby. Erich pounced on it but Jacob immediately came at him. It was now the keeper's turn to try to escape. Jacob attacked wildly, trying to bite his hand, but he warded him off with the broom. The problem was how to keep hold of the baby and open the patent lock on the door. At the last minute, the keeper hurled the broom at Jacob's face. This sent the big rhesus sprawling. Erich got through the door in time to slam it in the face of Jacob, who was left on the other side, storming with rage, still with the broom.

The infant rhesus was given the name of Sibyl. She was only about six hours old when she was rescued. Erich wrapped her in his jacket and hurried over to the warmth of the office buildings. The attendants examined the little monkey all over and no one thought she had any chance of surviving. Her eyes were closed and she made no sound; weak from pain and cold she had apparently lost conscious= ness. The small body was covered with bruises, black patches and open wounds which scarcely bled. It was blue with cold and the clinical thermometer showed that it might just have come out of a refrigerator. But its heart was still beating, so there was still hope.

The lady director of the Heidelberg Zoo at once telephoned to the children's hospital in an effort to arrange for the baby rhesus to be put into an incubator. She implored the senior physician to admit it for premature birth treatment but he refused to give his consent. The rhesus was full of germs and monkeys are automatically suspected of tuberculosis. He was extremely sorry but he could not sanction the use of sterile equipment. The zoo officials naturally understood his point of view but they were determined not to be beaten. They arranged electric fires and radiators. They carefully massaged the little monkey and, with its heart still beating, they laid it in a small wicker basket. The nursing experience of the female staff was called upon and a consultation took place. It was decided that baby's milk should be given in a doll's feeding bottle which held a fraction of a pint.

The infant Sibyl suddenly opened her eyes and began to cry. She had never known her own mother and she was now surrounded by human mothers who were all full of compassion for the baby monkey. The women declared that she was crying for her mother but, in fact, she was hungry. When the rubber teat of a doll's bottle was pushed into her mouth she stopped yelling. Then, for want of anything better, the end was perforated and stretched over the bottle. Would the infant suck? Everyone bent anxiously over the cradle. There was no need to worry: instinct works very surely. As long as the foreign object was warm and soft, it was all the same to the infant rhesus, who sucked and sucked. Before the bottle was finished the baby collapsed from exhaustion but long and regular breathing reassured the onlookers. The first battle had been won. The improbable had happened and a sigh of relief went round the room.

A day and night watch was organized on a rota. The small creature was safely over the first hurdle and its life then followed the normal routine for a suckling infant: a feed every four hours, with a gradual increase in the amount, and a warm bath between the first and second feeds. Young Sibyl made such good progress that when she was fourteen days old she made her first attempt at crawling. Her attendants were astonished to see her lying on the warm carpet of the director's sanctum, going through exactly the same motions as does a human child. She lay on her belly and shoved herself along, pushing herself forward with her feet.

Every now and again she came to a full stop and lay there, exhausted, having a little nap. Day by day her crawling improved. This type of activity had never been observed in the zoo enclosures because a rhesus baby normally clings to its mother's belly.

A few weeks later Sibyl was able to climb on to the chairs and table and she could already run quite well on all fours, as befits a rhesus monkey. She naturally developed more slowly than if she had been with her mother because there was none of her own kind to imitate. But in spite of having no one to show her how, she was soon able to explore the whole room from carpet to chandelier.

Inborn behaviour patterns are very powerful and the time had now come to give Sibyl a change of living quarters. She had never become house=trained. A monkey quickly learns the easiest way to evacuate itself and, unlike a chimpanzee, it has not the mental capacity to understand that nappies and close=fitting pants are not meant to be removed. Most monkeys are tree=dwellers and it does not matter where their excrement falls in their natural surroundings. Some time ago an animal trainer named Guldan, of the Krone Circus, tried very hard to solve this problem. He provided each chimp with a handsome chamber=pot in their sleeping quarters, and as a result of his training they understood that they must sit on the pot — but they never grasped for what purpose. On occasions something would by coinci= dence drop into the pot and, when this happened, the trainer hoped that he was achieving his goal. But his optimism was, unfortunately, ill=founded. Every monkey keeper is faced with this problem. He is continually cleaning up after his animals and no place in the monkey enclosure is free of fouling. His colleagues in the big cat house have a much easier time in this respect.

What with gymnastics on the curtains and chandeliers — not to mention other matters — it was obviously time that young Sibyl should be moved from her nursery. She was given a nice roomy parrot cage near the entrance to the zoolo= gical park so that she could watch the visitors as they came up to the pay=desk. It was hoped that she would be less lonely if she could always see humans from her cage. Her sleeping place was also changed. She had already chosen to crouch in her basket rather than to lie down, a crouching position being characteristic of her species and clearly inborn. In her new quarters she crouched on a shelf. She lacked, however, her customary source of warmth because there was no coverlet in her parrot cage. Her attendants had noticed how she always liked to sleep with either the coverlet or the pillow pressed against her belly, as though she needed specially to keep this part of her anatomy warm. Under normal conditions an infant monkey sleeps belly to belly with its mother, the infant being protected by the warmth of its mother. Sibyl's human parents, however, had a bright idea based on their observations and experience. They decided that camel hair was the warmest substance and so Thusnelde's thick winter coat was plucked and a mass of it stuffed into a net bag. This was given to the young rhesus in her new sleeping quarters and she accepted it without ceremony, pressing it to her the very first night.

When I got to know Sibyl she was exactly six months old. Up to this time she had never set eyes on a monkey. She looked upon humans as her natural com= panions, she played with human toys and live dogs and birds which were human pets. Could one say that she was imprinted on man? Sibyl was not in the slightest bit shy with humans. Everyone who resembled her attendants was loved passion= ately by her. She demonstrated her affection for people in typical monkey fashion, driven by her instinct. Whenever she could, she sat on the shoulders of a human friend and inspected his scalp. She went through his hair, strand by strand; next, she examined the corners of his eyes searching for the so=called sleep matter and for scurf on the eye lashes; finally, after examining his nose, she turned her atten= tion to his mouth. Her grooming act always ended in removing any particles of food from between his teeth. Not everyone is willing to submit to such a minute in= spection without batting an eyelid but Horst, the son of the lady director at the Zoo, was quite content to be given the full grooming treatment. It was he who had watched over her during the first days of her life, sitting by her basket and never letting her out of his sight. He now took her for walks — without any chain or lead — through the Heidelberg Zoo.

It was thus that I was introduced to Sibyl. Horst told me her story while she sat on his shoulder and groomed him. I particularly wanted to see where she had been born and so the three of us walked to the open enclosure where the rhesus monkeys lived. The nearer we got to it the more peculiarly Sibyl behaved. She climbed down from Horst's shoulder and squeezed herself between his hip and arm. We paid no attention to her climbing at first but when we were about twelve feet away from the enclosure, the little rhesus trembled like an aspen leaf. "Look at this," Horst exclaimed, "she's dead scared," and he lifted the little creature up high, holding her between his thumb and index finger. She appeared to be transfixed, as though frozen stiff, and she had turned her head round, as far as she possibly could, away from the monkeys in the enclosure. Two of them had come over to the wire=netting, full of curiosity. They were Mimi and Jakob, her natural parents who had behaved so unnaturally when she was born.

It was obvious that Sibyl was terrified of her own kind. She had never seen monkeys before and, owing to the peculiar circumstances of her upbringing, she regarded humans as her own kindred and had attached herself to their world. Horst then turned Sibyl to face directly towards her parents but she twisted her head so far round, like an owl, that we were afraid she might break her neck. So we walked quickly away from the terrifying place. Sibyl behaved as though she had just been given a reprieve and instantly did gymnastics down the trouser=legs of her foster=father. But she stopped just before she reached the bottom. She looked anxiously in the direction of the enclosure and then clung very hard to Horst's leg. It was as though she had intended to scamper about on the ground but had not completely recovered her confidence after the fright. Presumably one would never be able to keep Sibyl with other rhesus monkeys.

On the day of my visit Horst had parked his motor=scooter in the usual place in front of the zoo office. Sibyl was quite familiar with the shiny chromium monster as she had already perched on Horst and been driven several times round the zoo. On our return from the monkey enclosure we sat on a bank in the sun and Sibyl, all her fears forgotten, climbed on the scooter. She clambered all over it in a completely carefree manner and I took a number of photographs. She then climbed over the clutch and took great interest in the handle=bars. She stood up on the right=hand side, exactly in front of the mirror, and suddenly flinched as though she had been struck. She let out a yell such as I had never heard before from a rhesus and sprang from the handle=bars in a frantic leap. Later, when I developed my films, I found that I had only caught the tail end of her flight. She then came stumbling over to Horst, her limbs all stiffened, and clung to him with her heart beating at an alarming rate. What had happened? Had she received an electric shock from the metal parts? We investigated the motor=scooter but found nothing wrong. But something had frightened her so much that she had nearly had a heart attack. My photographs provided the explanation. Sibyl had looked into the driving mirror and without any kind of warning she had suddenly caught sight of a monkey face, her own reflection. This must have given her as great a shock as when, only a few minutes earlier at the enclosure, she had seen a monkey for the first time in her life.

CHAPTER 21

Lord of the Island

THE SUN WENT down behind the small island in the deer pool of the Kronberg Reserve. The hubbub of an official opening ceremony had died away and the island now belonged to the gibbons. Four of them had been moved with consider= able difficulty to their new home on the island in time for the inaugural celebra= tions. Press, radio, television and newsreel cameramen had all done their work and, together with the guests of honour, departed after the official ceremony, leaving the island to the gibbons and their keeper.

In spite of the lateness of the hour the gibbons showed no inclination to enter their house. It was not considered wise for them to spend the night out in the chilly air and it was reluctantly decided to catch them in nets. The two younger animals and a somewhat tame female all went into the net quite quickly. A large black male named Samuel, with white hands and feet, was not such an easy propo= sition. He worked his way through his entire acrobatic repertoire high up in the two tall trees on the island. No one dared to catch hold of him with bare hands because every time anyone came too near he bared his teeth, opening his mouth wide to reveal his terrifying canines. It was already dusk when Samuel was brought in.

I visited Kronberg a week after the opening and was introduced to the gibbons by Fritz Walther, the director of the Reserve. Three of the gibbons were inside the house. More gibbons had been transferred to the island but three of the origi= nal four had steadfastly refused to leave the house and explore the island. We went inside to see them: two bashful blondes, Hau=hau and Mühmchen, sat in one section, while Samuel, a big black gibbon, climbed hand=over=hand in the other. The hatch door leading out into the fresh air was wide open but the square aper= ture seemed to act as an invisible barrier, pressing the gibbons back into their house.

Fritz Walther wanted to continue his rounds of the Reserve and, as I hoped to spend the entire day with the gibbons, I escorted him back over the bridge and then locked the gate. As I returned, two graceful little brown animals, Tschi=Tschi and Bubi, came darting over the bridge to meet me. Their long slender arms reached down to their ankles, and as they waved them daintily in the air, they looked like two butterflies frolicking about in the sunshine. They came up to me and we all three sat down on the warm sand and talked to one another. Bubi played end=

lessly with my camera cases, investigating them but never succeeding in getting them open — a chimpanzee would have had them undone after a few minutes. Tschi=Tschi sat on my lap. She embraced me with her slender arms and pressed herself against my breast. She began to breathe very deeply and rapidly. Gibbons have the lungs of an acrobat and I could hear the air pumping into her lungs quite audibly. Then she shaped her mouth like a tube and started to sing: "Huuuuu=huuu," holding the vowel for a long time. She breathed faster and the sound came in shorter bursts and in a higher pitch: "Huuu=huuu=huuu." In a rising crescendo, spanning higher octaves, the "Hu" hammered in my ears and suddenly ended in a triumphant, squealing "Huiiiiii!" which reverberated along the walls of the house and echoed in the distance.

Samuel's black and white face peered through the hatchway with a puzzled ex=pression, caused perhaps by Tschi=Tschi's song. I walked slowly across the bridge to him. He remained sitting in the hatchway, holding on inside the house with his left hand while fingering the outside wall with his right hand. It looked as though he was not prepared to risk putting his whole body outside the house. His head came out for a moment but he immediately ducked as if fearing that a bird of prey was diving above him. Later in the evening this behaviour was explained when Fritz Walther told me that there had been a particularly excitable man standing on the ape=house roof during the catching operation.

I sat down quite close to the hatchway and did nothing in particular. I spoke quietly to Samuel and without haste. Occasionally I looked at him and then away again. I was in no hurry. Only time and a restful atmosphere could restore his confidence. I did not attempt to do anything with him. I do not know how long I remained just sitting there quietly but suddenly I felt a very soft pressure on my left arm. Samuel's white hand lay along my lower arm. I looked at him but he looked past me and acted as though he did not see me. His hand scarcely moved but his long fingers moved idly over my arm. I did not stir. I was quite satisfied, the long wait had brought its own reward.

After a while I moved very carefully a few inches away from the hatchway, increasing the distance between us. Samuel shuffled restlessly on his seat and once again the hunted look came over his face as he glanced upwards. But there was nothing to alarm him and everything remained peaceful. He hung his right leg out of the hatchway and moved forward, coming just far enough to put his hand on my arm again. Gibbons can give a nasty bite but I forgot all the warnings which I had been given about their unpredictable tempers and, taking his hand in mine, I shuffled along on my seat without letting go of him. His left leg came out through the hatchway. I took a deep breath. Dare I take the decisive step? I looked at my watch. Two hours had gone by. I decided to risk it. I put Samuel's hand on to the wooden planking of the bridge and I moved a suitable distance away from him. Either he would come over to me or I would have to start again right from the beginning. I called him: "Come on, Samu, come on." "Tschi=tschi=tschi," came his reply and he sat beside me as though it were the most natural thing in the world. He had left the dark hatchway two yards behind him. "Well done, Samu," I said and put my arm round him. He could easily have sunk his canines into my flesh. After another hour we got up and walked hand in hand over the last six yards of the bridge. Once on the island Samuel forgot all about his fears and romped about with the other two, leaping about in the branches and uttering joyful screams as they played a game of tag.

It was not until three months later that I was able to pay Samuel another visit. He greeted me so warmly and demonstratively that the shy Mühmchen followed behind him and then sat down below me. When I stretched out my hand towards her, however, she jumped up and ran off, looking anxiously at Samuel. He showed his teeth, threatening me quite clearly with pointed white canines. But the threat did not last long and he continued to sit beside me. Mühmchen then lay down in a heap of green leaves and put her arm under her head. Samuel ran over to her and she immediately sat up and started grooming him. It was quite obvious that the little blonde was under his protection.

A fortnight earlier there had been an addition to the island population. A big black gibbon named Pedro had arrived from Bangkok and had threatened to upset the social order. He was as large as Samuel, with the same white hands and feet, but instead of a white mask the white circled his head, making it look as though he were wearing a black skull=cap. Pedro showed a weakness for the blonde Mühmchen right from the start and he began to assess Samuel and to weigh up the position. I sat down with my cameras right in the middle of this drama and I could sense the tension in the atmosphere.

Mühmchen squatted in the foliage in front of me and a light wind stirred the leaves, so enabling me to see her. Pedro came swinging through the branches, making his arrival in a provocative manner. He held on with one arm above Mühmchen, swinging to and fro and reaching out towards the object of his desire with his free hand. He was challenging Samuel, who sat a short distance away and never took his eyes off him. Then Pedro let go and dropped down into the leaves beside Mühmchen. This was too much for Samuel. Waving his long arms he was on top of them in a single leap. His teeth gleamed and he roared at Pedro as he gave him a terrific box on the ear. Pedro sprang out of the branches and landed defensively on his knees. He held on to a rope as though it were a life line and his eyes showed fear. Still smarting from the blow, he took his revenge and attacked Samuel. Blows rained from all sides as Pedro screamed with rage. Each one tried to seize the other's neck and press his adversary's head into the sand.

Mühmchen sat in the middle of the turmoil as though nothing were happening. She drew her legs up, put her arms round her knees and rested her chin on her left hand, watching the contestants. Samuel's teeth flashed but suddenly he was down and Pedro knelt on him, screaming as he struck blow after blow. But Samuel went for Pedro's hands and feet with his teeth, holding on for a fraction of a second wherever he could make contact. So Samuel fought his way out and sprang at Pedro, seizing him with a hold that was worthy of an exponent of classical wrestling. He then chased him away as though he were a bothersome fly. Pedro eluded him by a bold leap up into the branches and then, with his limbs flying in all directions, he hurled himself down on to Samuel. But the latter saw him coming and delivered a well=aimed kick at his belly which virtually finished the fight. Pedro had had enough and, seizing a rope, he made his exit screaming. Samuel aimed blows after him but Pedro was well beyond his reach.

Although the fight had raged backwards and forwards quite close to Mühmchen, she had not moved from her place. She had merely lain on her side to get a better view. Her face showed no emotion or concern for the two males battling for her favours and the outcome of the struggle appeared to leave her quite unmoved. When Pedro fled into the house Samuel sat down close to her and scratched his chin. He was quite content, there was no doubt that he was still lord of the island. The blonde rolled over as though waiting for someone to take notice of her. Samuel spat angrily. Alarmed by this show of temper Mühmchen sprang to her feet and, in obedience to the monkey code of behaviour, she started to soothe him. Squatting down beside him, she parted his long black hair and cleaned his white skin, picking out scales and particles of dust. Samuel lay on his back, his limbs stretched out, grunting with pleasure. Pedro sat in the hatchway at a safe distance, and waited for another day.

CHAPTER 22

When a Chimpanzee "Weeps"

WHEN A HUMAN being wants to make contact with an animal, he naturally uses words, the medium of communication with others of his own species. Very few animals understand even a tiny fraction of the human vocabulary and these are all domesticated — dogs, horses and cats. Their understanding of what humans say to them is basically a response to known auditory and visual stimuli. Strictly speaking, it is no more than a reaction to training and this is true even of a dog, where through constant use the response may border on understanding.

Animals do not have a language in the sense that this term is applied to humans. There is still no way of translating the human vocabulary into animal language. It was more than a hundred years ago that Arthur Schopenhauer wrote that an animal communicates its feelings and moods by gestures whereas man communi= cates his thoughts mainly by speech — or hides his thoughts from others by speech. He also pointed out that hearing is not synonymous with understanding or per= ception, which signifies an awareness of thoughts communicated by words. Scho= penhauer's words retain their validity today, although man still uses words to communicate with animals. Nevertheless, it is the tone of his voice and not the words which is significant as far as the animal is concerned.

Animal trainers spend hours at a time standing in front of the cages of newly= arrived carnivores in order to "converse" with them every day. Similarly, a fal= coner who wants to "man" or tame his bird of prey will take it for long walks on his arm, talking continuously. The purpose of all this talking, which is virtually a one=way conversation, is simply to accustom the animal to the sound of the human voice. It aims at getting the animal to differentiate between praise and censure by the tone of voice and eventually to incorporate the master's voice in its sphere of comprehension.

At the same time, we must also adapt our eyes and ears to the "speech" of animals if we want to understand how they express themselves; it is essential to make precise observations on how they "converse" with one another. Once we know their methods, the investigation of their "speech" or language of communi= cation becomes considerably easier. Students of animal physiology and behaviour have worked on this subject for more than half a century and as each year goes by they astonish us with the results of their research. One such language which

has occupied man since the time of Darwin is that of the anthropoid apes. Scien=
tists were faced with difficult problems right from the start and R. L. Garner's
The Speech of Monkeys was written under conditions of unspeakable hardship in
the forests of Central Africa. The American Robert Yerkes worked for decades on
research into the language of anthropoid apes, especially that of the chimpanzee.
More recently the American scientists Keith and Cathy Hayes reared a female
chimpanzee as though it were their own child, naming it Viki, and giving it the
freedom of the house. Viki lived on intimate terms with them for eight years and
during this time she learnt to speak only three words: "Mama", "Papa" and "Up".
She adopted many human habits, being a remarkable imitator, and she also ap=
peared to understand a great deal. Viki Hayes died of meningitis in 1955. Could
it be that man had demanded too much of the animal?

Our detailed knowledge of the language of animals has advanced considerably
since Schopenhauer's day but the fundamentals have not changed. Animals cannot
make thoughts audible in speech, they can only express momentary feelings. But
the range of animal language is in a way more extensive than the human one
because animal "speech" is not restricted to the tones of the larynx: it may em=
brace movements of all the limbs, as when they drum, rattle, beat, tap or stamp.
Well=defined movements and postures effectively reinforce audible speech in this
way, more than they do in man.

It is generally accepted that anthropoid apes supplement their speech by re=
markably effective grimaces. It is these which give them such a human appearance
but they are, in fact, very misleading. The anthropoid apes are the most similar to
man of all the creatures which have evolved and, because outward likenesses exist,
we frequently tend to look for parallels and interpret a chimpanzee's expressions
along similar lines to those of a human being. Nothing could be farther from the
truth. Scientists have been aware of this for a long time but the facts are not
generally known to the general public. I have often stood in an ape house in a zoo
and witnessed misinterpretations of this kind by the public. A visitor will roar
with laughter at an ape which, although it looks as though it is laughing, is actu=
ally "weeping". No drama results from the misunderstanding because the ape
cannot get out and the visitor cannot get in, but it is a typical example of how
humans fail to understand animals. A few seconds later the same ape may well
by romping about happily with his companions, showing no signs of distress.

An ape's mood changes quickly and the mood of the moment is reflected in its
facial expression. A whole gamut of sensations may pass over its face in such
quick succession that, although the apes may be described as our first cousins, we
have difficulty in following the fleeting expressions. There are only two facial ex=
pressions which have much the same meaning as human ones: embarrassment and
deep resentment. When we are puzzled we scratch our chins or rub behind our ear
and we tend to pout our lips; anthropoid apes express their feelings in similar
human=like gestures. Other expressions, however, which pass over the wrinkled
face of a chimpanzee bear no relationship to the human interpretation which we

erroneously give to them.

Although I had a large collection of ape portraits with widely varying expres=
sions, they were all of different apes in different situations, and I decided that
when there was a suitable opportunity I would get as many different expressions
as possible of the same ape. I had to wait a long time — years in fact — for a con=
venient occasion. It happened one morning in the Hellabrunn ape house while I
was watching the reactions to his keeper of a four=year=old chimpanzee named
Moritz. I had only my miniature camera with me but the light was quite good
and other conditions were favourable. Moritz was on a bench with a wall behind
him so that he could not move away and, as he did not want to leave the bench
on which he was sitting, to some extent the range was fixed.

The keeper ordered Moritz to move but the chimp merely answered "Uuh=uuh",
expressing surprise and friendly amusement by pushing his lips without showing
his teeth or gums. Moritz was telling the keeper that he did not think he really
meant the order to be taken seriously or at least that the keeper could be coaxed
out of it. When the keeper made no response to Moritz's laughing gesture, the
chimpanzee became embarrassed. "Oooh=ooo=ooh", he went as he drew in his
head. I noticed that he rubbed his chin and lower lip, making a displacement ges=
ture which was typically human. Moritz was not quite sure whether to ignore the
keeper's instruction or not. The keeper gave him a sharp reminder: "Go to your
place, Moritz." The chimpanzee pouted and from his rounded mouth came "Huuu=
uuu=Huuu=uuu!" This expression is a preliminary either to joy or rage and simply
reflects excitement. In this case it was meant to be quite friendly. Transition to
the next stage came with the closing of the lips, followed by a grimace exposing
the teeth in the lower jaw, while "Hu=uuu" rose in pitch. This was an expression
of friendship which might rapidly develop into real ape laughter. Moritz tried to
coax the human to make contact and his hand moved towards the keeper's face,
his fingers seeking the man's mouth. But the wheedling had no effect and back
came the stern command: "Move over, Moritz, go on, to your place." Moritz was
quite offended by this and I knew I could expect some reaction. Angrily he showed
all his teeth. By baring all his teeth he was not laughing but expressing ape rage.
Had he been laughing only the teeth in the lower jaw would have been exposed.
"Ho" and "hu" rose an octave and the "Huu" changed into a high=pitched "Huuuui=
uuuui=Huuuuuii". In a matter of seconds the little ape had whipped up its anger,
working with his whole body. He did not seem to know what to do with his
hands but he expressed his rage by stamping both feet on the bench and shrieking
louder and louder, "Hiii=iiih=hiii", in an even higher pitch than before. The keeper
shouted at him to sit down and raised his hand threateningly. The chimp sat down
but the shrill scream increased in volume so much that it was almost unbearable
to human ears. Then Moritz tore at his own hair and seized both his ears, pulling
at them as though he wanted to wrench them off — a most painful display to
watch. His mouth was wide open. The chimpanzee was "weeping", but no tears
came. Apes do not have the psychological release mechanism for making the tear

glands function which humans are equipped with. The glands are present but they function only for the purpose of keeping the eyes clear.

In less than a minute I had taken twenty=two exposures, each one of them a fleeting expression on the chimpanzee's face. The quarrel between the ape and the man had ended with the ape sitting where he was told. It had lasted under a minute. Had Moritz been a human, he would have brooded over what had been done to him and his facial expression might well have reflected his memory of the incident, but chimps respond to each moment as it comes and they cheer up imme= diately harmony is restored. This is equally so whether the ape's relationship concerns a human being or an object.

CHAPTER 23

How Not to Become Leading Ape

I STOOD IN an empty enclosure in the zoo one day, waiting to meet a troop of young chimpanzees. As they were let into the enclosure, they rushed towards me like a gang of children just let out of school after the last lesson. They stormed me like a horde of bandits seizing a fortress and I was an easy target for them as I stood in the centre of the empty space. Four of them were already clinging to various parts of my anatomy, when the chief female, Jenny, sprang on top of me and almost knocked me off my feet. Jenny, who already weighed a hundred-weight, was most determined in her efforts to establish her superiority over the other youngsters. She did this in a most ladylike manner. Having leapt at me she did not openly set about the others as a rumbustuous child might have done in a similar situation — she was much more diplomatic — she believed in attacking on the flank and she carefully took my arm and bit it, making sure that I should pay attention to her. It was a warning, in effect: "Take some notice of me or else . . ."

At the time, all I could do was to turn towards her. Mausi, the next in the hierarchy, sat close beside Jenny and she went into a sulk. She would have liked to command my attention but as her senior in rank was in a quarrelsome mood she did not dare do anything about it. She did what most humans will do in similar circumstances: she put on a face which implied that she could not be less interested. She stuck out her lower lip and looked sulky, just as we do when we are not too pleased.

The attackers came from all sides and, as there was a considerable weight hanging on to me, I had some difficulty in keeping my balance. Moritz, the young chimp whose facial expressions and speech I had studied earlier, clung to my stomach in the typical position of a youngster seeking protection from its mother. Moritz was not aware that Jenny had succeeded in capturing all my attention by her tactical bite and he tried to reach my mouth in order to touch my lips with his index finger. He wanted me to talk to him and to shape my lips into a gesture of goodwill. All of a sudden he stuck his finger in my mouth. I could do nothing about it except spit. Moritz did not object to this, he had reached his goal and I had not bitten his finger. In fact, everything was fine as far as he was concerned; he had even triumphed over the leader, Jenny, and he pressed himself still closer to my stomach.

In the meantime Katia did what she always attempted to do when there was a male human visitor to see her: she climbed on my back and peeped down my collar. Katia had a different approach for her female visitors: she would lift up the hem of their skirts and look underneath. Konga, the lowest in the hierarchy, did not dare risk entering the mêlée.

Suddenly the whole situation changed. Mausi gave up sulking and suddenly leapt on to me. Moritz fled in the face of this threat gesture and Mausi clung round my neck, looking down on Jenny and gloating — or so her expression ap= peared to me. It was too much for Jenny and she gave me a painful bite on my index finger to re=establish her superior rank. I felt that this was going too far. If I were to avoid becoming a shuttlecock between Jenny and her subordinates it was time that I intervened. A powerful cuff over the ears, in appropriate chim= panzee style, restored order.

The load of chimpanzees was pretty heavy and I sat down to recover my breath. Keeper Neidl thought I had had enough and asked if he should call a halt to the proceedings. I told him I wanted to continue a little longer to see what would happen if I did nothing to defend myself. The keeper was afraid that I might not emerge all in one piece and took a firm grip on his rubber truncheon.

I sat and did nothing while the young chimpanzees did everything. Laughing and chattering, they dropped on to me. Each one tried out his strength on me and it was not a very gentle exercise. They would never have dared to try this with their keeper because he was acknowledged as the "ape boss". With me, they were trying to establish my position in the social hierarchy; it was all a matter of pres= tige and this was naturally important even to the lowest in rank. Jenny resumed her biting: her teeth seized my upper arm and tore my shirt. Mausi bit my knee. Moritz tugged at the other shirtsleeve and Katia, the inquisitive youngster, perched helplessly on my back in the general confusion. Suddenly Konga saw a chance to rise in rank and she sprang at me from behind. I could expect nothing good from her sudden attention and so Neidl intervened. Had I wanted to become the "ape boss" I would have had to behave in a much more brutal and drastic manner and act like an ape amongst apes — but this had never been my intention.

This pale blonde is an almost white=haired gibbon and answers to the name of Mühmchen. She is a lar gibbon living on the ape island in the Kronberg Reserve for Animal Research.

The gibbons of south=east Asia with their elongated arms are the most elegant monkeys in the world and they are also the masters of three dimensions. They have conquered the air above their territory right up into the tree=tops. Watching their seemingly weightless swings one feels that they could be in flight.

Samuel, the white=handed gibbon, who looks rather like an Eskimo in an anorak, is master of the ape island. He is the protector of the pale=coloured Mühmchen. When Pedro arrived later on the island, he cast an eye over the little female and fights ensued. Samuel boxes his opponent's ears, kicks and bites and he soon gains respect by these methods. The body of this monkey is held in a peculiar position in that it moves and runs upright. On account of two rump callosities and certain other differences the gib= bons are no longer regarded as anthropoid apes.

1

Which one is laughing? 1. Moritz is puzzled: he sticks his index finger in his mouth.
2. Lips pushed forward, teeth and gums covered: smiling astonishment.
3. Tube-shaped mouth denotes excitement: he may be happy or angry.
4. This is how Moritz laughs: lower jaw exposed, upper jaw covered.
5. And this is how chimpanzees cry – as humans laugh.

3

If one gives a group of chimpanzees a free hand, one can never become their "leading ape". Each one tries to get the newcomer *below* him in the hierarchy. Senior ape Jenny shows her superior= ity by biting my hand; Moritz sticks his index finger in my mouth: a declaration of loyalty; Mausi, the number two in the group, bides her time; but Konga, the lowest in the hierarchy, suddenly sees that the time has come for her to rise in rank.

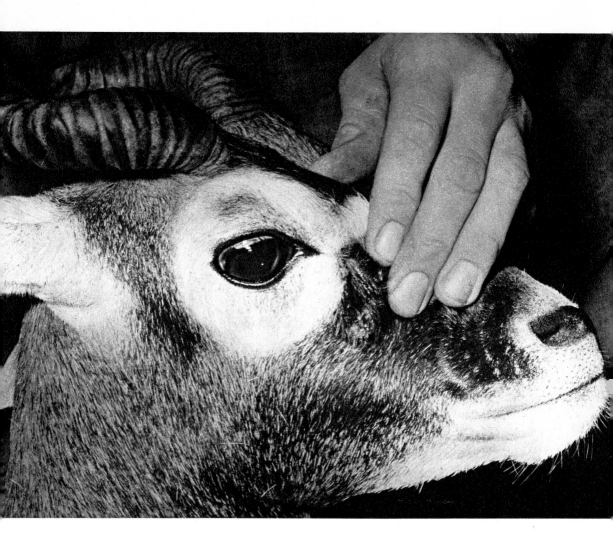

An animal is not as free to roam in the wild as one might imagine: when a lynx walks through the forests, he will soon get what is coming to him from other members of his species, because even a lynx does not like to see a stranger suddenly appear on his home range. The wanderer is well advised to lift his nose into the wind and take the scent, in case there is an airborne message: "Private ground. No admittance." Lynxes and many other animals exhibit "name= plates": they mark their territory by rubbing prominent places with scent and they check the efficacy of the scent from time to time — like the bear in the Zurich Zoo seen on the left. The Indian blackbuck marks with a special organ, the pre=orbital gland. Peccaries, wild pigs from Central and South America, carry a volcano=like organ on their backs for this purpose (photograph and enlargement on next page). The common roe deer has three such scent factories: one on its head (photographs above and on p. 237) and two on the hind feet.

No animal lives without orderliness: this pair of rhinos in the Munich Zoo began to divide up their territory as soon as they had been let into it (left above). Permanent paths join fixed places at which definite acts are performed at definite times: drinking (1, 5), bath (2), siesta area (3), toilet area (4), playground (6), sleeping quarters in the den (7), lavatory (8), grazing ground (9) and feeding place (10). These locations are only reached by paths A, B and C, with a roundabout (D) to avoid unnecessary encounters. Hein and Muschka at the feeding place (below) and at the roundabout (right). Unless compelled to do so, the animals will not leave their paths.

Paths and locations are used exclusively for well=defined purposes. A rhino would never degrade its feeding place or siesta area (above) into a lavatory (below). The lavatory is also a sign of possession and this is made even more effective by the rhino scattering the excrement with its back legs. The lavatory is placed where a stranger is bound to encounter it in the immediate vicinity of the door. As the animals stand in the toilet area, cattle egrets are available for hunting parasites just as they do in the wild (right).

The lion Brutus is group leader of the mixed carnivores trained by Trubka.

◄ On the rhino playground: after their midday siesta the animals like to romp around with their keeper. African travellers are sometimes sent off on a journey with the advice: "If a rhino attacks, wait till the last minute and then step aside; it will either turn aside before it reaches you or rush wildly past you." I have never tried this experiment in Africa because the dents on the mudguards of my truck show that some rhinos react differently.

CHAPTER 24

There Are Limits to Freedom

IF WE IMAGINE that free=living animals can wander at will throughout the whole range of their natural habitat, with nothing to hinder their choice of move= ment, we are indulging in an illusion. Research over the last fifteen years has brought to light some surprising facts about the conditions under which these animals live. The lynx, for instance, is not free to roam through the forests of Alaska. The whole surface of an extensive lake is not open to the free=flying swan, and a squirrel may not leap from branch to branch throughout the entire wood. These are only three examples of animals which appear to be free to move as they choose in their natural surroundings.

Many animals have a permanent territory which they defend savagely against members of their own species which are of the same sex. A great tit may live close to a chaffinch or blackbird in the nesting season, but if another male of the same species appears in the territory, it will be driven off at all costs. Members of other species are tolerated and in some cases even welcomed. For instance, as a human being, I am pleased to see members of other species sharing my garden but if a stranger comes to stay, uninvited, I do not take kindly to this invasion of my home.

Humans mark their territories quite clearly by giving their houses names or numbers. Nothing is left to chance in the world of humans but how is an animal to know that his neighbour's home area starts at the next tree? Humans proclaim their tenancy visually. Birds use their voices primarily, announcing possession audibly, while some mammals follow yet another method: they set boundary marks with scent. They make their own odoriferous substances and mark specific places with it. Tiny traces of the scent stick to tree trunks, to bushes and to rocks or stones. Visiting members of the same species perceive these scent marks just as clearly as a human would see a notice "Private property. No admittance." Each mark has its owner's particular scent, as specific to its owner as the names on our

Tigress Mirza is the only lady in Vojtek Trubka's group – and she is well aware of this. Typically feminine, she loves being flattered and sulks if spoken to sharply. And she is always unpredictable.

visiting cards. The same scent persists throughout the owner's home range and, although humans cannot smell it, a wanderer of the same species picks it up without any difficulty.

Professor Heini Hediger, Director of the Zurich Zoo, has studied this subject intensively and published some remarkably interesting data. When I went to see him he spent some time explaining the individual characteristics of his animals to me. Animals in captivity also mark their own property and I hoped to observe this in the Zoo.

In the early hours of a dull morning in August I climbed up the hill to the bear pit in Zurich. When I was still some distance away I noticed two light brown points standing out above the top of the wall: two ears of a bear on the alert. At the edge of the pit I saw the impressive outline of a brown bear. He was sitting on the same level as me and only a ditch separated us. I had expected the bear to beg for food as soon as I appeared, which is what they usually do whenever the public approaches them, but this one did nothing of the kind. He remained sitting down and his wet nose wobbled about as he took scent. From the look in his small eyes, he did not appear to be aware of my presence but looked through me into space.

It was very early in the morning, possibly too early for begging to be on the timetable. Visitors to the Zoo mostly arrive somewhere around eleven o'clock and from then on food=begging naturally becomes the main occupation for the rest of the day. It looked as though I had come at an inconvenient time for Master Bruin, who was expecting his keeper to be bustling about.

Professor Hediger established certain patterns of daily activity as a result of detailed observations which he made on the everyday life of animals. Like many other creatures, the bear had his daily routine and he had no intention of allowing me to interfere with it. He continued to look into the distance beyond me. I had been standing in front of him for a quarter of an hour when he suddenly heaved his massive frame on to all fours and trotted off into the farthest corner of his run. Here he put his nose up and sniffed, reaching up with his whole body as though drawn by a magnet. He stood on his hind=legs, twisting his nose upwards all the time and breathing violently, sucking in air and exhaling it again. There was a dark patch on the wall and his nose travelled over this area like a vacuum cleaner. The patch was his mark, the place where he announced: "My territory begins here." He was testing whether the scent mark was still sufficiently strong. Did this walk to the corner of his home ground mean that he was put out by my presence? Perhaps he wanted to see if the boundary mark needed renewing be= cause I had stood on the edge of his home ground for so long. Or, could it be a displacement gesture because my presence embarrassed him?

A bear places his warning signs at various points on his boundary. The scent naturally loses its strength in the course of time and it is checked and renewed on tours of inspection. The bear in front of me was renewing the scent now. He turned round and rubbed the bristly hairs on the nape of his neck against the wall.

The scent was already in the hair, which had been previously saturated in a urine bath. The bear then turned round and sniffed the patch again. This time he was satisfied with it and, growling, he dropped down on to all fours. With my feeble sense of smell I noticed nothing, but the bear in the neighbouring den would undoubtedly have been alerted; once he had taken the scent, he not only would have known that he was in foreign territory but would also have received certain other information. In the wild the intruder would then have to consider whether it was worth provoking a fight or whether it would be best to make himself scarce. A female bear will know from the scent mark that a potential mate is in the vicinity even though she has not seen him. Only the male has the right to leave scent marks. Before my bear returned to his seat he defaecated ostentatiously against the marking place, thereby exhausting all the possibilities of his scent factory.

Professor Hediger explained the behaviour of bears to me along these lines but other observers have come to completely different conclusions — among them Dr Peter Krott, who reared brown bears and attempted to establish them in the Italian Alps. According to these experts the bear has no territory in the wild, it does not have boundary trees and it does not mark a territory at all. Bears in the Zurich pit undoubtedly mark, but could this behaviour be conditioned, perhaps, by captivity? These apparently conflicting opinions will only be resolved after many more detailed studies have been made in the wild and in zoos.

We already have some information, in the same field, about other animals which have glands for scent=marking. Professor Hediger took me to see one of these animals — a peccary — in a small paddock in the Zoo. He opened the gate quietly. "If you move quietly, they won't go for you," he said. I was standing in a small field and there was a narrow, well=trodden path ahead of me. It was one of many which the collared peccaries — a wild pig from South America — had trodden in the long grass. I could not see any of the animals but I watched the various paths, knowing that the peccary moves only along tracks, never leaving them unless forced to do so. The path went out of sight among some fir trees. A low grunt came from this direction. Then a pale pink snout appeared, showing its typical nostrils as the animal came towards me. Above the long snout two ears were held out like conch shells, ready to pick up any sound that came from me. The dark grey and white creature came trotting towards me on its short dark legs. It tripped along with short steps, sticking strictly to the path; its small hooves did not break a single blade of grass beside the track. The peccary could have shortened the route by cutting the corners, but it kept to the path as though it were running along a railway line, unable to leave the rails. Professor Hediger described this as "route compulsion".

It was arranged that I should stand on the path to see what the animal would do. The wild pig stopped in front of me. The route continued farther but I was blocking the way and this made him hesitate. He could have gone round me and continued on the path but he gazed up at me and then turned round swiftly. I heard a low murmuring sound like the wind rustling through corn. The spiny dorsal hairs quivered on the back of the bristly little animal and opened up like a rosette, exposing a black mound on the top of the back. I looked down on a miniature volcano. A little white point appeared on the summit and the volcano started to spit. A white secretion spurted up at me. The scent gland of the peccary was operating. The wild pig was obviously treating me as though I were a strange male peccary approaching and, by his action, he was preventing me from walking along his route. Suddenly he broke away and left the path, a type of behaviour which is normally the result of pressure or fright. But presumably it was because the territory on either side of the path had not yet been made "taboo". The grass, bushes and trees in front of me were now marked with the secretion. Through my entry into the paddock, the peccary's territory had become smaller. The boar evidently did not think much of his chances of driving me away like an intruding peccary and so he marked the new boundaries with scent as I stood there.

The wiry hairs on the boar's back slowly sank down as the stock of scent was used up by the large demands made on it. The boar retreated into the wood. He did not trot back directly across the grass where he had just made his marks but went back at right angles to his path and then made off into the wood. In this way he held me in view all the time and could see whether I was following him. I then went back the way I had come and stood outside the fence, watching to see what he would do next. As soon as he saw me, he came galloping along the track, showing no sign of hesitation and not moving as cautiously as he had done before. He stopped a short distance from me and then sprayed the fence with his last reserve of secretion so vigorously that I had to step back to avoid getting my trousers marked with scent.

The natural scent secretion for marking is produced in diverse parts of animals' bodies. In some cases it comes from the bladder or gut, but if the scent is a glandular secretion from the skin the glands may be found anywhere between the head and the feet, according to the species. For example, the European roebuck and other species of deer release scent during the rutting season from glands situated on the hind hooves. In addition, the roebuck has another gland which is situated on the forehead between the antlers. Some people think that the well-known "fraying" action is nothing more than marking with scent.

The red deer's scent factory is situated a little lower down, in the pre-orbital glands. Many antelopes also produce scent under their eyes. A strong-smelling "grease" is produced and smeared onto branches, twigs and tree-trunks in small quantities, usually not larger than the head of a matchstick.

Professor Hediger also took me to see a blackbuck. Naturally he could not guarantee that this animal would be as obliging as the collared peccary. The blackbuck only marks during the rutting season, when marking not only serves to advertise territorial boundaries but also presents a scent which entices the female. An animal will occasionally mark if something unusual occurs and this was what we hoped would happen when I set foot in the blackbuck's paddock. The keeper accompanied me, armed with a strong broom, for he knew his Pappenheimer. "He

will go for any stranger in the enclosure," he said. "I have had some mad esca=
pades with the Professor's zoology students. They run like hares in front of the
buck and if any of them gets caught they are 'spiked'. Injuries from its horns can
be dangerous and trousers have been torn on many occasions!"

We approached the paddock by way of the den. As soon as it saw me the
antelope came galloping across. It immediately attacked with lowered head,
thrusting its pointed spiral horns towards my thigh. I was still in the den and I
had to catch the buck by his horns and with the keeper's help remove it from the
den and push it outside. The buck attacked again and again and this went on
for some time. The keeper stood outside, waiting to help ward off the attacks
which were aimed at me. I did not dare go outside, and under such conditions I
was hardly likely to observe any marking and photography was certainly out of
the question.

After one of these attacks we managed to keep hold of the buck, which was very
annoyed. The keeper showed me the pre=orbital glands and I succeeded in taking
a photograph. The gland in this animal was so large that the keeper's whole thumb
sank into it. We then let the buck go and it came rushing back. It stopped short
of me, looked, but did not attack again. Had he given up? Perhaps he realized that
I could not be removed by force; what could he do now to show that he had the
right to this particular area? Then, just as I had hoped, the blackbuck showed his
characteristic way of marking territory. He walked quietly up to the keeper's
broom, laid his head against the handle, tilted the upper edge of the pre=orbital
gland against the wood and smeared a sticky secretion on to it, rubbing his head
slowly up and down. It was as though the blackbuck were saying: "This is my
broom, I am the only one who is allowed to play with it." Then he rubbed the scented
grease on to the other side of the handle with equal precision. Suddenly he moved
his head right up to where the keeper had his hand and smeared this. Was the
buck implying that the keeper belonged to him too? The keeper sniffed at his hand
and then held it out to me. I perceived a slight irritant, a scent not unlike formic
acid. The buck had not finished. He pressed the gland against the keeper's trousers
and then stepped up to me and marked the door of the den. This appeared to
satisfy him and he bounded away with the typical springs of blackbuck. The keeper
excused himself as the buck, now expecting a game, stood waiting and pawing the
ground with his front hooves. The keeper knew that he was asking to be petted.
He tickled and scratched him and then ran off, with the buck following in huge
leaps. I was no longer of any importance to the animal. The taboos had been laid
and these should hold me. With its scent secretions the blackbuck had banned me
as precisely as the peccary had done.

In an animal's home range, widely distributed scent marks work in much the
same way as the walls of a house. The animal feels safe and secure when it is at
home and only goes outside the range very unwillingly and if forced to do so.
The idea of settling down into a home is very familiar to us as humans but we

cannot turn animals into humans by assuming that they have similar ideas. How does an animal settle into its home? Does it, in fact, ever settle down?

One can easily observe how animals make themselves at home, in a concen= trated form, when they are living in zoos or reserves where the restricted areas allow everything to be seen. The captive animal brings with it the inborn charac= teristics of the species and transfers the habits of its free=living relatives to the enclosure with which it is provided. An animal in captivity is relieved of two of the greatest pressures of life in the wild: the need to find food and the need to watch for enemies. In a zoo, food is provided and there are no enemies to avoid; an animal can make do with a much smaller area. Other problems of daily life, however, also occur in captivity. All animals live very orderly lives and only abandon their routine under pressure. They perform definite acts at definite times in definite places. Professor Hediger says that animals are subject to a strict "space= time" system.

I photographed some examples of this in Zurich but there was no opportunity to watch any new arrivals settling in, and for this I went to the Munich Zoo at Hellabrunn, where a new rhino paddock was due to be occupied. This was ideal for my series of observations as I could be present from the start and watch the new tenants in effect unpacking and settling in.

Nine months earlier a pair of half=grown black rhinoceroses, named Mushka and Hein, had arrived at Munich from Hagenbeck's Zoo in Hamburg. They had spent this time inside their house, becoming familiar with their new quarters and getting to know their keeper while the outside paddock was being prepared. Now the animals were to be let out for the first time. "Open the door and let out Mushka first!" came the instruction. Keeper Hermann slipped the heavy bolts and slowly opened the thick, armoured door. Mushka stood in the doorway, sniffing and breathing in the fresh air. The area of the paddock was over 3,000 square yards and it was covered with thick green turf right up to the edge of the water= filled ditch which separated it from the public. A soft green carpet awaited them in the warm spring sunshine but Mushka seemed to be afraid of the expanse in front of her. She was nearly two years old. She stood in the doorway with her head up and her nostrils distended as she took the scent of this strange new world. Keeper Hermann tried coaxing her but she kept hesitating. Every time she went to put a foot down outside, she drew back again into the house. Hein was still confined behind another door and did not know what was happening. He showed his annoyance by banging his horn on the door. "Hurry up with Mushka," someone shouted, "or Hein will have the door down!" Hermann did his best but no man can make a rhino move if it does not want to. He held out some fresh green beech leaves just in front of Mushka's nose. This helped and Mushka lurched forward, her body half outside. Then Hermann walked backwards a few paces and the rhino followed very cautiously. Every time she took a step forward she stopped and took scent from all directions. It was not the proverbial picture of a captive animal rushing to break its way out of confinement.

The inner den was nearly a hundred square yards in area and during the pre=
vious months neither of the rhinos had tried to use its strength to break free from
the house. This was hardly surprising. They had no desire to change their com=
fortable quarters, where they were well fed and warm throughout the winter. The
floor was heated to a controlled tropical temperature and infra=red heat was
supplied from above. The only complaint which the rhinos might have made was
that Keeper Hermann never spent enough time with them. He was always having
to go and attend to other animals, and when he left them they whined in a high
voice.

It took over an hour to get Mushka just a few yards away from the house on
to the turf. In the meantime Hein had become fractious. Were they trying to take
his Mushka from him? Hermann could not get the door open fast enough and
Hein squeezed himself through a narrow chink. At the doorway he took one short
sniff and, seeing Mushka standing there, he rushed outside to join her.

A few days later the rhinos were satisfied that the open paddock contained no
enemies and they overcame their original shyness of this new=found freedom.
The pair now began to see how they could get comfortable. They raised their noses
frequently and, after they had determined the general direction of the wind, they
began to divide up the three thousand square yards of their territory. I soon
noticed that the grass was trodden down in certain definite areas and in some
places completely flattened. The grass elsewhere was as though it had never been
disturbed. Two months later the divisions of the paddock were apparent even to
a layman. Paths joined the rhinos' favourite resting places. There was one path
which ran from the den to the feeding place; this was double=tracked and the
rhinos always trotted along this side by side. The path then went on to the drink=
ing place and bath or to the browsing area. Another path led from the playground
which they had established, across the toilet area to the place where they took
their siesta. Narrow paths ran from this area to a place which the animals had
sensibly sited on the edge of their territory, namely the lavatory.

Nobody had told the two rhinos how they should divide up their living space.
Mushka and Hein had made up their own minds and acted accordingly. It was
done in the same manner as that which their parents adopted in North Kenya.
They never departed from the paths they had made. If the keeper called them
from the side, they would make a detour to reach him rather than step off the
path. They were "house=trained" and would never defaecate or urinate in any
place other than the one they had set aside as the lavatory. It was interesting to
note where they had positioned this. They had chosen the site with thought — or
should we say by instinct? — and it was in the only possible place from which
a strange rhino might approach, close to the door of the den. Hein and Mushka
also marked the boundaries of their home range with their own scent. This meant
"no admittance" for anyone other than Keeper Hermann.

In the wild, rhino marks are valid only for other rhinos. They are of no signi=
ficance to other animals with which they live, such as elephants, zebras, giraffes,

hippos, gnus and lions. The taboo of one species does not apply to others. At Hellabrunn, Hein and Mushka demonstrated how they divided up their territory within the invisible walls of the scented boundaries. This kind of division is also true of rhinos living in the wild, as I know from experience. When watching at Lake Kahn, on Mount Meru in Tanganyika, I observed that there was only one wallow for three rhino territories. The three rhino families had to come to some kind of settlement about how it should be used. They either had to use the wallow at different times or argue it out. I watched and photographed both procedures from a seat high up in an acacia tree. Fights for the wallow were always between males and they were primitive in character. From my high perch I could hear the clash of the double horns against each other, but no blood was drawn and after the exchange of a few blows the weakest usually acknowledged the position and withdrew.

Animals make a home according to the manner of their species, and in this they are like humans. They may have the equivalent of a bedroom, dining=room, playroom, store or larder, bath, lavatory and connecting corridors. Each place is used for its exclusive purpose. It is out of the question, for instance, for an animal to sleep in its "dining=room" or turn its "playroom" into a lavatory. Can it be said, then, that there is no difference between a human and an animal home regarding its sub=divisions? It cannot. There is one place which an animal home lacks — the fireplace — and this constitutes the basic difference between the two homes. A place for the fire has always played a dominant role, even among the most primitive members of our species. And as Professor Hediger pointed out, the difference is a significant one. In a sense it is the most significant difference between man and animals, since the mastery of fire was not only the beginning of man's technical progress but also of all human culture associated with technological development.

CHAPTER 25

A Pyramid of Personalities

VOJTEK TRUBKA, a leading circus trainer on the Continent, believed in training his animals by the gentle methods originated by Carl Hagenbeck. He was a master trainer who was a dogged supporter of these training methods in spite of the fact that he had received many injuries, particularly to his hands, which were constantly in danger. He started working with beasts of prey when he was seventeen years old and he had been injured on more than twenty occasions. In one incident, during a performance, his left arm was severely lacerated by a tiger. But even after this unpleasant experience, he could not bring himself to give up his occupation, as it would have meant saying good=bye to his animals.

Trubka was a powerfully built man with broad shoulders. He conveyed a sense of authority and toughness. He was also a great showman and was clad entirely in white for his performances, from the tips of his fingers to the soles of his boots. At the start of his act, the ring would be in complete darkness except for a power= ful spotlight which played on his white figure.

The enormous golden=red curtain did not quite cover the entrance to the dark tunnel which led out of the ring and was connected to the cage where his animals waited. Behind the scenes, at the end of the tunnel, Keeper "Tiger Heinz" would stand listening for the instruction to release the beasts of prey. He had been with Trubka for twenty=five years and had looked after all the various carnivores which Trubka trained for the circus. He had served the master trainer faithfully in a long association.

Another performance was about to begin. A hush fell over the audience as the spotlight played on the powerful physique of the figure in white. Trubka stepped lightly into the centre of the cage. "Let them out," he called in a husky voice. The keeper slid back the bolts of the travelling cage. Three splendid tigers and three magnificent lions trotted quickly down the dark tunnel out into the pool of light.

"On your mark, Brutus! Caesar! Prince! Go on, Bengali! Get along there, Cam= bodia! Come on, Mirza!" All the beasts jumped instantly onto their pedestals. Once again the great performance started, a performance which is always a test of authority and which can so easily become a matter of life or death.

Trubka started his act by building a pyramid of his lions and tigers. The animals all went quietly to their allotted positions, obeying the trainer's instructions in=

stantly. From the layman's point of view it all looked very simple but appearances are deceptive. When a situation is under control, it is all too easy to imagine that the animals are so docile that there is no danger of any kind. In fact, the pyramid is as explosive as a powder keg, waiting for a spark to ignite it. Something of the tension conveys itself to the audience in spite of the calm demeanour of the master trainer.

I watched Trubka give more than fifty performances with his carnivores, and I learnt a great deal from him as I talked to him during training sessions and in many rehearsals. During this period I got to know the individual lions and tigers. At first I found it difficult to tell one lion from another and the tigers all looked the same. After a while, however, I was able to distinguish each animal by its individual behaviour. Each one had a particular character with a well=defined per= sonality. They had different temperaments and these became apparent as I watched their reactions and the way in which each one behaved.

Trubka had known his animals from birth, as they had all been reared by him. From an early age the animals had been accustomed to one another. They were allowed to run and play together before they were a month old. It was at this early age that Trubka introduced them to the pedestals which would one day be their seats in the circus arena. A young animal at play displays its own individual tem= perament, and the experienced trainer spends a lot of time watching his animals closely, assessing their characters and deciding how to fit them into a group act. When he feels that he knows each individual trait of character, he decides on the position each one will occupy and shows them, as part of their play, their places in the pyramid. Observations made at this stage determine the eventual positioning of each animal in the pyramid. Animals of very different temperaments sit close to each other in the pyramid. A small mistake made in the handling of any one of them may spark off trouble which is lying below the surface, waiting to burst out. The pyramid is an explosive structure and it cannot be held for any length of time. The trainer cannot afford to relax his concentration, even for a fraction of a second, if he is not to lose control of the entire group.

Trubka built his pyramid in this particular act on an arched bridge. The tiger Cambodia had a completely sanguine temperament and occupied the first position at the base of the arch on the left=hand side; moving up the arch, the leader of the group, who was a choleric lion named Brutus, had a seat which came next; the central position at the top of the arch was occupied by a tiger called Bengali, an animal of distinctly phlegmatic temperament; coming down on the other side was Caesar, a lion with a lot of sense, and next to him, completing the half circle, was Mirza, an unpredictable tigress; finally, there was one position right under the arch of animals and this belonged to the melancholic of the group, a lion named Prince. The position allocated to Prince corresponded with his rank in the social hierarchy.

Each animal had been accustomed to its position over a long period of time and the detailed arrangement of the pyramid was never altered. Custom, habit and routine are the trainer's chief allies in every performance. By never changing their positions, the trainer knows automatically where each animal is and he can keep a watch on the trouble spots. He must know from which direction danger is liable to threaten. By constantly being on the alert, he can sense when an individual animal is getting restless and feeling unsettled. A good trainer is always aware when trouble is brewing between any of his group.

Trubka placed the phlegmatic tiger, Bengali, between the group leader, Brutus, and his nearest rival in the social order, another lion called Caesar. The choleric Brutus was thus separated from his rival Caesar. The presence of the tiger between these two lions acted as a kind of barrier, both of them seeing the tiger as an obstacle preventing any direct method of settling their differences, such as having a go at each other in the ring. This tended to make both of the lions turn Bengali into a kind of whipping boy and they were always liable to make the tiger an excuse for trouble. For this reason Trubka never once took his eyes off the animals at the top of the pyramid.

A trainer, however, cannot afford to concentrate on just one or two of his animals. The next most likely trouble spots were at the base of the pyramid, where the two tigers sat on either side at the front of the arched bridge. It was very easy for the sanguine Cambodia to irritate Brutus; with his nervous temperament, he was rarely settled and only too ready to become restless and upset. On the other side at the base was Mirza, a typical female of the jungle who was always quite happy to have a go at her lord and master from behind. Trubka had no illusions about Mirza's temperament, and he knew that she would seize any opportunity to attack him. Prince, the grimly introspective coward, was the only one from whom there was nothing to fear. Every evening the pyramid of personalities was held in position for six to ten seconds only. While Trubka cracked his long whip over their heads the animals sat quietly but he dared not take the risk of holding this explosive structure for too long.

Trubka had a special knack of speaking to each one of his big cats in a voice that was appropriate to its temperament. He would speak constantly to all six, addressing each one in the tone of voice to which it would be most likely to respond, switching automatically from one voice to the other as he called them by their names. It was during the finale of the performance that Trubka talked to them continuously, giving a glittering display of his brilliance as a trainer.

The act finished with the animals walking backwards round the ring, retreating before their master, until eventually they were in a position to back out of the ring, returning to their cage at the end of the dark tunnel. Completely absorbed, the audience saw the three tigers walking quietly backwards. Cambodia, Mirza and Bengali fell back, step by step, before the advancing figure of Trubka; face to face with him, they watched every movement that he made and listened to the sound of his voice. He addressed three personalities, three temperaments, and he dared not make a single slip of the tongue. He used a quiet voice for the sanguine Cambodia, a coaxing tone for the unpredictable Mirza and a harsh voice with a hard, uncompromising stare for the phlegmatic Bengali.

The audience watched spellbound as the animals retreated slowly but there was scarcely one person under the big top who was fully aware of the reckless nature of the performance taking place in the cage in the arena. To appreciate this, it is necessary to know something of the psychology of the big cats. The public's attention was undoubtedly rivetted on the performance in the circus ring, but they knew so little about the animals they watched that they did not understand the degree of skill and knowledge being displayed by the trainer in front of their very eyes.

Biologists have recently shown that there is a certain distance at which big cats in the wild must either advance to attack or retreat in flight from man. This distance factor is age=old. As Trubka advanced on his tigers, he was driving them into their "inner circle". By reducing the distance between him and the animals, he was entering the forbidden zone, and thus forcing them to attack. In spite of his proximity, however, Trubka's tigers did not strike back but retreated slowly, step by step. Why did they not react and attack as would have been inevitable in the wild? Trubka's explanation of their behaviour was very simple: "I have endless patience with them." But this could not be the complete answer.

Trubka's tigers were fully grown — they were all nine years old — and Professor Hediger's intensive research has shown that what appears to be the flight distance in adult animals is in fact something rather different. He says that, when the animal becomes fully adult, it loses its youthful tameness and becomes less approachable. Trubka's tigers were trained to do this act when they were very young and they were probably docile from long familiarity with their master. It is also possible that their behaviour may have been due to the fact that they were born in captivity and had, therefore, never experienced the true flight distance as a constituent part of their life. Perhaps the age distancing, as postulated by Hediger, did not apply in their case. We still do not know the answer. When I talked of this to Trubka and asked his opinion, he merely shrugged his shoulders. He had never had time to seek for scientific explanations of the basic motivation underlying the behaviour of his animals, he merely knew his own animals through constant contact with them. He was with them day in and day out and he worked with them by "feel", knowing each one intimately. This kind of secret bond between an animal trainer and his charges can probably never be subjected to scientific analysis.

Trubka displayed outstanding powers of concentration. He had nerves of steel and he could never afford to be ill. The animals were quick to notice the slightest indisposition on his part. Even a cold, a headache or a stomach upset was sufficient to encourage Brutus to challenge Trubka's position as "human alpha animal". The readiness to fight for social re=grouping is always smouldering below the surface in a group of big cats — and human indisposition can provide the conditions in which it can suddenly burst into flames.

Vojtek Trubka was firmly of the opinion that the man who wants to be a successful trainer must be a first=class example of his own species. The acclamation of the crowd must be subsidiary to the fascination which lies in the struggle for supremacy between man and beast.

In his view there are ten golden rules which a successful trainer must observe:
1. Love the animals and the work.
2. Have patience beyond patience.
3. Have nerves of steel.
4. Know the minds and habits of your animals as well as you know your own.
5. Be conversant with animal hygiene.
6. Be physically and mentally strong.
7. Have the ability to teach.
8. Have presence of mind.
9. Possess the temperament of an actor.
10. Order your own life well.

CHAPTER 26

The Appeal of a Nursery

LION CUBS ARE like magnets: people find them quite irresistible. Every zoo director knows the effect of a litter of cubs on the public. Publicity men are also aware of their value and well=known personalities are often photographed with a cuddly cub. Private people keep them as pets and many more would have them if they could. I would like to do so myself. The public flock to see them at a zoo or circus. They hold up their children to get a better view, with a chorus of: "Aren't they sweet?" What they would really like to do is to get at the cubs so that they could release their urge to stroke and fondle them.

I am no different from anyone else and my reactions are just the same. What is it that makes us want to behave like this? It is purely instinctive. The "caring= for" drive is released in humans by a number of characteristics which are present in very young children. If these same characteristics are shown by other living creatures or even by dummies, such as toys, the caring instinct is released. We find young ducks, baby rabbits and young cubs particularly lovable and attractive. The same characteristics also influence the choice of domestic pets, particularly by women who treat them as substitutes for children. Pugs and pekinese arouse this emotion to a greater extent than the long=headed breeds such as dachshunds or wolfhounds. Round=headed animals such as cats and parrots also stand high on the list. The names given to animals often reflect our affectionate attitude to them: Squirrel Nutkin, Brer Rabbit, Robin Redbreast are all examples of this.

What are the particular characteristics which release this drive to look after and care for something which appeals to us? The head must be round, whether it is a child's or an animal's, and the eyes should be large and set just below the centre of the face. The human heart is touched by a convex forehead, a chubby face and short, plump arms and legs. In experiments with dummies, children react only when the above characteristics are present. This is the secret of why some toy animals are loved and others are not.

A lion cub embodies all these appealing features. It also has one other charac= teristic which should not be overlooked: a fine soft fur, inviting our fingers to stroke it. In spite of all this, it is not advisable to stroke young lions. The lioness keeps a watchful eye on her offspring and, should a visitor stretch a hand towards the cage bars, she comes straight over, spits and bares her teeth in a threatening manner.

But there are many things to see in a zoo, and people only stand and look at the lion cubs until they are satisfied and then wander away. If they stayed longer they would be fascinated by the lioness's way of looking after her cubs. Cleanliness and orderliness are the rules observed in the nursery. Play and training alternate in strict rotation with mealtimes and periods of sleep. There is much that is similar to life in a human nursery.

We still know very little about the habits of animals and few people can spare the time which is necessary for detailed observations. Neither the director of a zoo nor the keepers have time to undertake intensive studies of this kind. Their day-to-day work keeps them fully occupied and this field of research is left primarily to scientists who specialize in animal behaviour.

The young Swiss zoologist, Dr Ernst Inhelder, recently sat up for many nights in the lion house at Basle Zoo making observations on the sleeping animals. His notes show that the father lion is a lazy fellow by night as well as by day. He sleeps for longer periods and more deeply than his mate. He not only leaves the lioness to provide food — in the wild — during the day but he also leaves her to keep watch at night. According to this report the lion is scarcely entitled to the title of King of the Beasts which we have given him so arbitrarily, and we ought to adjust our mythical view of the lion in view of the facts now being presented to us by the scientists. The key to knowledge lies in observing behaviour. To find out more about lions we must spend more time watching lions and analysing the results.

I decided to spend a whole day in a lion nursery, watching in much the same way as a behaviour scientist, and one spring morning I took a garden chair into the lion house at the Munich Zoo and sat down. There were two cubs in the nursery, three months old. It was 6.30 a. m. when I started my observations and the session lasted ten hours. It sounds simple but a lot of preparation was necessary. It took me a whole week to accustom the lioness, Penny, to my presence with photographic equipment. I had photographed her frequently during the previous year, so we were not strangers to each other, but since then she had given birth to the two cubs and an invisible barrier had sprung up between us. At first, she was not prepared to allow me to photograph her offspring while she was looking after them and as soon as I approached the bars of the cage she rushed forward, shielding the cubs with her body. As I had no intention of taking photographs with the bars in the foreground, I had to get her accustomed to my putting the equipment through the bars. After the first fruitless attempt I paid regular visits to the nursery, appearing with all my equipment three times a day. In this way she gradually accepted my presence and eight days later she was so used to me that she took almost no notice of me and carried on with the rearing of her family undisturbed by my proximity.

I then sat for ten hours watching her daily routine with the cubs and making notes. During this time I learnt quite a lot about the duties and problems of a well-ordered mother of lion cubs. The entries in my notebook looked like this:

06.30　Penny ready to spring out of her sleeping quarters, as usual; she did not spring but never took her eyes off me; followed each movement I made putting the camera through the bars but did not spit or growl and remained lying down. Cubs scarcely noticed me, merely stretched their limbs while sleeping; they are influenced apparently by Penny's quietness. Can take photographs holding the camera inside the bars, watched by Penny all the time.

06.55　Cubs begin to romp and chase each other in a mock fight; no deference shown to their mother, collide with her frequently as they race about; no reprimand from Penny; hectic chase. Cubs squeeze under Penny, forcing her to get up. High=spirited romp of youngsters, who jump on mother's back and climb partition to neighbouring cage, where Sultan, their father, lives.

07.48　Penny back at her sleeping place; has apparently had enough of the cubs' romping.

07.52　Cubs somersault in the hay in their sleeping quarters. They let themselves flop and breathe heavily.

08.10　Cubs press hard against Penny, they want a drink; she lies on her side reluctantly. Loud smacking of lips as they are suckled; Penny watching me all the time. As cubs are already being weaned I am very pleased at getting suckling photographs as late as this. (Penny has been getting them on to a flesh diet this week.)

08.17　Suckling finished; cubs lie beside each other, away from Penny. Their eyes close to slits, blink sometimes, eyelids droop but eyes open wide at any unfamiliar sound. Doze for more than two hours.

10.51　Cubs stretch and leap out of sleeping quarters in one bound. Very energetic, trot all round the cage, exploring every corner. Appear to devise pranks. Notice my flash equipment at the bars and begin to investigate it, nibbling at the leather straps. Penny, not sure what they are doing, spits and growls. One cub pays attention and stops playing; the other one carries on. She comes over; it stops playing; she cuffs it and picks it up by scruff of neck and carries it away dangling between her paws. She washes

The animal trainer has to take into account the physique and character of each animal when training it for a circus act as well as being careful not to destroy the social interdependence of the group of animals. The fundamental characteristics of each animal determine its role in the act. Above, from left to right on the arch: the tiger Cambodia (sanguine), the group leader – lion Brutus (choleric), tiger Bengali (phlegmatic), lion Caesar (sanguine), tigress Mirza (unpredictable). Underneath them all, the lion Prince (melancholic). On p. 262 tiger Cambodia jumps through the hoops – Page 263 (above) Every evening it must be made clear to the group leader that the trainer is master. (Below) The trainer gets them to walk backwards round the cage by playing on each one's individual personality.

If one spends a little time in front of the lion cubs in a zoo, one can often witness the way in which young carnivores are brought up. It is important that lion cubs should learn how to hunt as quickly as possible, because without prey they cannot feed. The hunting drive is inborn and is released by any movement.

In Augsburg Zoo the two cubs of Marcus and Fanny snatch awkwardly at everything which moves: to begin with it is the long tail of a parent with its exciting tuft at the tip.

264

The lion cubs are not yet three months old and their teeth are as sharp as needles. For some time the father lion has been finding the game with his tail irksome. In an effort to finish the lesson in hunting prey quickly, he withdraws the teaching aid and hides his tail under his body. But the young rascals are getting quicker and over and over again give him nips which in the end make him stand up . . .

... and growl, and with a bad=tempered expression on his face he calls the young meddler to account. Frightened by the paternal rebuke, the cub crouches down (opposite, above). Fanny inter= venes immediately. Is she afraid for her cub, is Marcus's tone too rough? Before Marcus has time to withdraw she strikes him in the middle of his face with her large paw. He is startled but thinks it wiser not to retaliate, as he knows that a lioness with cubs is not to be trifled with. He sits down in his old place without a murmur. The two little pests have been waiting for this and start to chase his tail. Fanny watches attentively to see what Marcus will do. Then he has a brilliant idea — he sticks his tail out under the bar.

267

Carnivores born in the circus provide the rising generation of performers and they are the pupils ▶
who receive training in newly devised acts. The youngsters are given their first task at a very
early age, often at eight months, and they have to jump on to pedestals in the central cage.

The two lion cubs are still suckling but they are already showing interest in their mother's food.
Their tongues go over and over their lips in anticipation. The mother does not allow them to
share her meal and she bares her teeth and growls. It will be another couple of days before they
are allowed solid food. When the time comes to change from mother's milk to meat, the lioness
will place premasticated pieces in front of her cubs.

This is a typical expression of a captive carnivore expressing conflict. The man is too close. The leopard is provoked by his proximity and must either attack or flee, but in captivity it can do neither.

it with her tongue, first on its back and then on its belly; same procedure with second cub. Washing takes one hour.

12.00 Penny puts the cubs to bed. Mid=day rest.

14.30 Everyone wakes up. Lioness gets up and perambulates round the cage. Sultan stretches. Cubs come bounding out of sleeping quarters and run around. This lasts half an hour.

15.05 Youngsters suddenly sit down. Meat trolley clatters; keeper arrives with meat. Penny growls angrily at cubs, who withdraw into background and sit down again. They remain there while Penny eats. They creep forward stealthily. Penny appears to take no notice and they sit beside her, smack= ing their lips.

15.21 Penny stops eating and only gnaws at bones, pulls off scraps and tears them up into small pieces; she chews them and then spits them out, pre= paring the food for her young. The cubs tread restlessly with their front paws.

15.32 Penny releases the meat and the cubs pounce on it ravenously. Eating is still somewhat difficult, many of the scraps seem too big.

16.03 First cub finishes meat. Penny seizes the cub and cleans the fur on its head, removing scraps of meat; she massages the skin with her tongue by licking against the pile — this stimulates the circulation and digestion. Penny takes hold of the second cub, the first tries to continue cleaning itself on its own.

17.15 Washing and massaging finished. Strokes made by mother's tongue are clearly visible in cubs' fur. Youngsters indulge in wild romp.

17.47 Both cubs flop down in their sleeping quarters. They are so tired they don't even take time to get into a comfortable position but fall asleep immediately.

17.50 Penny lies down. Her eyes blink and close.

My records for the day were complete but unfortunately it had not been a particularly good day from my point of view because the cubs had failed to play their prey=catching game. Perhaps it was not down on the day's timetable. Later on, however, I saw this at Augsburg Zoo, where there were two cubs, one male and one female, both of them two months old and still at the suckling stage. Young as they were, they had already started to learn the first lessons of life through play. Their parents, Marcus and Fanny, were lying stretched out in the sun, dozing with their eyes half closed. Only their tails showed any sign of life, moving with an irregular rhythm rather like a snake. Movement of any kind stimulates prey=catching behaviour in young cubs. They will chase after leaves or feathers stirring in the wind, moving twigs or stones rolling along; anything serves as "prey" and if the objects do not move of their own accord, the cubs will pat them and then leap on to them. The tufts on their parents' tails are favourite targets. The tail may lie in a curve on the ground or be held up in the air; it may twitch slightly or thrash about, but if it moves it will be chased by the cubs. Through play the cubs are learning how to catch their prey and at Augsburg I saw how naturally this play=training takes place.

I am not sure that the parents consciously arrange this form of exercise for their offspring, I am inclined to think that it is all part of an inborn behaviour pattern which is released by the activity of the cubs. When the cubs romp about there is, inevitably, a great deal of movement. The adults watch every movement and be= come increasingly vigilant, expressing their alertness by the restless movement of their own tails and, if the cubs were not their own litter, they would undoubted= ly go off hunting. As it is, they lie still with only their tails moving — and the cubs pretend that the tails are prey and try to catch them. In captivity the lesson never advances beyond the primary stage. It scarcely differs from that in the wild except that the plains and the bush provide a greater variety of teaching aids: beetles, crickets, frogs and tortoises, to mention only a few, all provide the same stimulus as a waving tail=tuft.

In the zoo at Augsburg it was the long=suffering father, Marcus, who bore the brunt of the lesson. He went to lie down near the bars of the cage and swung his tail as he sat down. Immediately the cubs made a dash to catch it. Fanny, the lioness, appeared to incite the cubs to further efforts and one of them nipped Marcus's tail so sharply that he winced. The tuft still waved to and fro with the cubs chasing it. They divided the work between them: the little female went for the whole tail while the young male aimed at the tuft, which he managed to catch and hold on to with his sharp milk teeth. This was too much for their father. He turned angrily on his impudent son and bared his teeth. Fanny was suddenly there, spitting at him. Did she resent this paternal interference with her children? Before he could retaliate she had slapped him twice about his face. He looked just like a hen=pecked husband, resigned to his fate, as he went back to his place near the wire and lay down. Intentionally or unintentionally, he abandoned the lesson. Let the others move if they wanted to, he did not intend to be disturbed and he lay so that his tail hung outside the cage, out of reach of the little terrors. Now they could have a go at their mother. . . .

CHAPTER 27

Wild Beasts

RICHARD RÖSSLER was a lad of thirteen when his father apprenticed him to an animal dealer. I met him when he was seventy years old, but even at this age he still regarded himself as a youngster as far as training animals was concerned. Although he had been handling animals for fifty=seven years, he told me that he was still learning about them. He had worked for nearly all the large circuses of Europe, preparing innumerable groups of carnivores for circus performances, and he was regarded as a leading international trainer.

Rössler had a fanatical devotion to animals. From an early age, even when he was still only a pupil, he had been opposed to the harsh training methods which were used in France and southern Europe, some of which persist to this day. He hated any unnecessary demands on the animals and abhorred anything which savoured of striving after effect, such as when a trainer appears to be surrounded by a bloodthirsty group of beasts which are only waiting for an opportunity to tear him to pieces.

In spite of years of experience, there was one aspect of animal training which had persistently eluded him. It was his lifelong ambition to work with animals immediately after they had been caught in the wild. Strange as it may sound, he had to wait until he was sixty=nine years old before an opportunity occurred, at a time when he was working with the Gustav Brumbach Circus. This is the story of how he came to fulfil his life's ambition at such an advanced age and how he travelled to South Africa to collect some lions which had been caught in the wild by a big game hunter.

For a number of years Rössler had been working with the same three lions but they were getting on in years; they looked old and the public did not enjoy watching animals which performed in an apathetic manner. Rössler had realized for some time that he must get a new group together and start training them but he had been through so much with these particular lions that he was naturally reluctant to face up to the fact that they were no longer suitable for the kind of circus acts which the public expected.

Together they had endured the bombing in the war, somehow managing to live through it. After this they were faced with the chaotic conditions of the post=war period when food was such a problem. Rössler suffered great personal privation as he travelled through the Eastern Zone of Germany but he and his lions lived through these troublesome times together. There followed an epic dash for freedom when the whole circus succeeded in escaping through the Iron Curtain to the Western Zone. This escape story hit the headlines and the adventure of the circus was subsequently reconstructed for a film called *Man on a Tightrope*. The same animals took part in the re=enactment of their astonishing dash to freedom.

In view of all that they had endured together, it was not surprising that Rössler should be so reluctant to admit that his veteran lions were past their best as far as the public were concerned. He kept putting off the decision to start a new group, and it was not until one day in the late summer of 1953, when a letter with a South African postmark arrived at his caravan, that he knew the time had come to begin again.

The letter was from Frank Boswell, an old friend who had seen *Man on a Tightrope* in Cape Town. Boswell had recognized Richard Rössler in the film and had immediately got in touch with Twentieth Century Fox of Hollywood, who had shot the film in Germany and from whom Boswell obtained Rössler's address. They had last met twenty years earlier, when they had become firm friends, sharing as they did a love of animals. Boswell's letter contained the news that he was now a big game hunter and dealer, travelling with a circus in his own name.

When the letter arrived Rössler went to the boss's caravan and told him the news in great excitement. Herr Brumbach remembered Frank Boswell. Letters flew back and forth until one morning Herr Brumbach sent for his old trainer and, with a twinkle in his eye, he handed Rössler a telegram: "Offer five male lions stop seven to nine years stop caught wild — Boswell." Rössler looked questioningly at his boss.

"Do you want to go and fetch them?" asked Herr Brumbach.

Rössler managed to nod. He could hardly believe it. He had not dared hope for it and now, in his seventieth year, it looked as though his ambition would be fulfilled: he would have the chance to train wild=caught beasts. The tears ran down his cheeks. He would see his beloved South Africa once more. He had longed to return after serving his time in South=West Africa for four years, before the First World War, and now it seemed that his dreams would come true.

It was December when Richard Rössler went on board the *Ridderkerk* in Rotter=dam, equipped with an enormous shopping basket in the shape of a travelling cage. The 8,000=ton ship carried a mixed cargo. Many weeks went by and the weather grew hot before Rössler arrived in Durban. Frank Boswell had written to say that the animals would be with the show in Pretoria, about five hundred miles to the north=west of Durban. After a thirteen=hour journey the two friends fell into each other's arms. Boswell pressed hospitality on his old friend but Rössler refused to do anything until after he had seen the lions. The Boswell Show was on the outskirts of the town. The animal hunter drove his big Plymouth fast through the streets and drew up right in front of the cages. A small African boy opened the car door. Rössler got out and stood looking at the long row of cages: all of them contained lions, some of them with three or four to a cage and others with one lion on its own. They were magnificent beasts. There were so many that Rössler was bewildered. "Which are mine?" he asked.

"Take your pick, they were all caught in the wild," replied his friend.

The show was due to move on from Pretoria after a few days and Rössler was so fascinated by everything that he decided to travel with it. He did not want to just collect his animals and depart; he wanted to take his time and study his charges in detail. Time went by—in Africa it slips by almost unnoticed—and one morning Rössler announced his intention of feeding the lions. His friend remon= strated gently: "You are in Africa now and feeding is done by the boys. A white man cannot possibly do this kind of work." But Rössler refused to pay heed to such conventions. Feeding was the way to establish contact with the animals and he did not intend to be put off.

The African boys took furtive glances at the old white man and most of them thought he was quite crazy, but two of the Bantus seemed to understand what he was up to—Ngombe, who was once with a circus in Togoland, and Sefu, a boy from the Congo who had recently brought three trained elephants to the show from the elephant school at Gangala.

On the first day that he undertook the feeding, Rössler made a significant dis= covery. All the lions pressed forward to take the meat out of his hand. He thought that this was the usual feeding "scrum" but, as he looked down the row of cages, he noticed that, when the African boys went up to the cages with the meat in their hands, the lions at once withdrew to the back of the cages. Rössler sat down in the shade to watch the animals. He saw that the cleaning of the cages was very rough and ready. The Africans were afraid of the lions and so the lions raged at them: the rough iron bars pressed into their flanks, the grating gave them sores on their pads, and they frequently hit their heads against the sides of the cages as they threw themselves about. Rössler decided to pick his five ani= mals with the least possible delay and then look after them entirely on his own. Ngombe and Sefu could still help but they must not be allowed to go near the cages.

There were thirty=two lions to choose from and deciding between such magni= ficent beasts was an agonizing process for Rössler. But although it was not easy, he already had some idea of their individual temperaments and he selected those which had made a favourable impression when they were being fed. He then arranged for these cages to be taken out of the general row. The period of train= ing started with the separation of his lions from the other animals in the show.

He immediately gave his lions names: Sahib, Sultan, Spotty, Pasha and Mo= hammed. It was important that they should get used to the sound of the syllables and thus learn their own names from the beginning. The five lions were all in separate cages and, as Rössler only had one travelling cage with a maximum of three partitions, his first task was to get them accustomed to each other so that they would not quarrel amongst themselves on the journey to Europe. Besides it was not possible to detect the social hierarchy until the animals were all together in one cage. All this took time and it was important that nothing should be hur= ried. One problem after another cropped up and travelling from place to place in the heat of Africa did not make things easier. Nevertheless, in spite of the diffi= culties, Rössler derived tremendous satisfaction from his work.

He had selected fully grown lions. He wanted his animals to dazzle the public by their strength and beauty. A handsome mane was absolutely essential but wild lions from Africa do not normally have picture=book manes and their bodies frequently look scarred and mangy. The so=called King of the Savannah often has bare patches of skin where ticks have been thriving and the scars of fights scarcely enhance his beauty. Rössler knew what he wanted and he knew why he had chosen lions aged seven to nine years, but he had not foreseen all the problems which their maturity would present. His lions were all mature males and each one had tested his strength in the wild. Their outlook on life was already set; they knew their own strength and consequently they were much more dangerous than younger animals. On the other hand, their wildness had certain advantages from the point of view of training: their flight=distance, for instance, had not become confused by the confidence in humans which hand=reared animals gain in early youth. Carnivores born in captivity become astonishingly tame and, although this makes them very attractive, it can lead to difficulties in training. The young ani= mal regards man first as a playmate and later as a rival; with his thin skin, man is handicapped in either role.

Rössler's lions became much quieter under his care than under the African boys' and his scent did not appear to upset them. His first victory over his wild beasts had been won peacefully and quietly. They were now ready for the removal of the solid partitions which separated them. Rössler achieved this gradually, leaving only wire=netting between them. At this stage the animals could see and smell each other and Rössler was able to observe which of them got on all right together. Fortunately, his luck held and he did not have to exchange any of them. He allowed them a few days to get accustomed to one another, keeping them under constant observation, and then he put them all in one cage.

The weeks turned into months, and one day, late in February, Rössler decided that the time had come to start the long journey home. The Brumbach travelling cage was pushed into position but the lions all refused to leave their old home. Then Rössler remembered that his lions disliked the scent of the African boys. He called the boys over, and the lions, disturbed by the scent, moved into their new cage. The lions were ready and Rössler was ready, but as he said good=bye to Boswell the two old friends shed tears, and neither was ashamed.

Rössler boarded the *Ridderkerk* with his lions. The weather remained warm as far as Gibraltar and he had a deckchair in front of the travelling cage so that he could sit and talk to his animals. In spirit, he was already standing in the central cage of the arena, arranging the pedestals and directing each lion to his own. In the meantime Sahib had emerged as leader of the group. When all the lions had been put in one cage together, he noticed that Sahib would not tolerate any other lion taking the meat before he had had his share. It was still an open question, however, as to which of the others would come next in the social hierarchy. There was a lot to be done and Rössler took advantage of the long journey to talk end= lessly to his animals. He spoke to them kindly and also severely if they quarrelled too much over food; they reacted appropriately to praise and censure and he was also able to scratch them.

Rössler only left his deckchair between Durban and Gibraltar to get food and to sleep. But after Gibraltar the temperature dropped, the deckchair disappeared and thick canvas was draped round the cage to keep out the worst draughts. The ther= mometer read 14 °C below zero as the *Ridderkerk* tied up at the Ellabot Quay at Hamburg.

Brumbach went to Hamburg to welcome his old trainer back. "Magnificent ani= mals, Rössler," he said, "really magnificent. I had no idea that you would bring back such beauties." He offered to take Rössler in his car straight to the winter= quarters of the circus at Ebenhausen, but Rössler told his boss that he felt he must remain with his animals.

"What! In this temperature?" Brumbach asked.

"Yes, even though it is so cold," replied Rössler.

It was fiften hours later when Rössler reported at the former ammunition dump at Ebenhausen. The lions were a bit upset by the journey and by the change in climate. They had got colds and the vet came out from Munich every day to treat them; they responded quickly to antibiotics and after a fortnight were all fit and healthy again. Rössler had nursed them through this critical time with endless patience and devotion. Although the animals were fit again, he was still not prepared to risk having them in the rehearsal ring and he spent another six weeks following the normal routine of feeding, cleaning out their cage, and talking to them.

At last Rössler felt justified in taking the risk of trying his lions out in the central cage in the ring. Their own cage was pushed into the arena and securely tied to the bars of the central cage. All kinds of safety equipment were placed round the cage — water, wooden sticks, iron bars and pistols, all ready for imme= diate use. The lions clawed restlessly at the door of their cage. The old trainer stood in the ring holding a long whip in one hand and a wooden stick in the other, ready to ward off any possible attack. This was the moment to which he had looked forward all his life. Only a yard to one side of the door through which they would come, the elderly Rössler stood his ground and gave the order to release his wild=caught beasts.

The door sprang open ... but the lions remained motionless, none of them would take the risk of stepping outside. Rössler called them by name, coaxing them to come out, but there was no response. It is true that Sahib stuck his nose out a few times but each time he recoiled as though frightened of the unknown.

The lions had to be helped out towards the open door. Suddenly Sahib launched himself through the doorway. Only an arm's length separated the man from the lion as he sprang into the arena. Rössler stood quite still while Sahib streaked past him. For the first time he stood face to face with his lion with no bars between them. Now was the time to test his theory about the flight=distance. He fixed Sahib with his eyes but could not concentrate on him alone because the other four all came out, one behind the other: Sultan, Spotty, Pasha, Mohammed.

There was only a yard separating Rössler from his lions but he still made no move. He lost sight of Sahib momentarily as the lion went out of his line of vision for a second but he had him back again almost immediately. There was no need to worry: Sahib had moved as far away from the man as he could and the others had followed him. It was all working out just as he had planned. Rössler had won the first round.

The lions went into the farthest corner and watched uneasily. It was all very unpleasant for them. They were in a new territory and there were no bars between them and the man. Rössler did not go any nearer to them but he moved quietly about in front of them. The lions watched every movement that he made; they did not move from the spot but turned their heads, following him with their eyes. Rössler talked to them ceaselessly: "That was fine, my beauties. Just lie down quietly. Father won't hurt you, there's no need to get upset." He picked up the pedestals one after another and placed them between himself and the lions. The animals became restless: they stood up, pressing back against the bars, obviously wanting to get farther away. "It's quite all right, nothing is going to happen." Two of the lions lay down again but the others remained standing up, ready to spring.

The pedestals now formed a wall. Rössler called Sahib and touched him lightly with the whip. Sahib could not retreat from the unpleasant whip, the iron bars were already pressing hard against his body. He growled angrily and clawed at the thing which dangled in front of him. He made several more dabs at it before realizing that there was no sense in trying to hit the lash, which still waved about in front of him. Sahib watched as the trainer took a step towards him with his elongated "arms", holding up the wooden stick and the whip. Slowly Rössler approached. Sahib danced about and spat repeatedly. The other lions all stood up, thoroughly disturbed. The man came nearer and nearer to them. It was too much for Sahib, the man must be driven away, he was coming too close ... Sahib let out a roar and rushed towards the intruder but an obstruction met him. It was too wide to jump over but he landed on top of it and looked to see where the man had gone. When Sahib sprang on to the pedestal, Rössler had quickly moved aside and increased the gap between himself and the lion. The distance between them was no longer critical. Sahib sat waiting for the next thing to happen but Rössler had no farther demands to make of him. "Enough for today," he said. Sahib was the first to leap back into the smaller cage. He did so quite voluntarily and the others followed him.

One week later all the lions were sitting on their pedestals. It had been a decis= ive week and there had been no incidents. The rest of the work was purely a matter of routine for a man like Rössler who had made his name as a trainer in the central cage of the circus arena.

His life's ambition was fulfilled with the training of this group but, as it turned out, these lions proved to be his last. Five years later Gustav Brumbach's Circus packed away its tents for the last time and Richard Rössler retired to a well=earned rest. His once proud group had already been reduced to two. Sultan, Spotty and Mohammed had been unable to stand up to the rigours of the German winters and, in spite of medical aid, they succumbed. Sahib and Pasha were the only two left and these were bought by an animal dealer.

CHAPTER 28

The Uncanny Cock

YOU WILL NOT find Seewiesen marked on many maps but this secluded research station — more like a village than a scientific institution — is not very difficult to find. I visited it for the first time many years ago and when I asked the way I was told: "Take the Andechs road out to Starnberg and, after Landstetten, look out for a big curve in the road; at the end of it, on the left=hand side, there is a narrow white board with black letters. It says M.P.I.V. *(Max Planck Institut für Verhaltensphysiologie).* Follow the M.P.I.V. signs."

That was a long time ago and I have now been to Seewiesen so frequently that I am no longer conscious of the signboards. There are other signs, however, which I look out for and these change with the seasons. In the autumn, roedeer stand in the clearing between the forest and the lake. In the winter, if I slip off the one=track road and follow the winding track through the birch trees down to the frozen rushes, I am certain to see a fox, sitting like a statue, watching one of the innumerable fieldmouse holes. And in the summer, does and fawns are always grazing in knee=high grass where I turn off the main road.

As one emerges from the silence of the forest, it is difficult to realize that in this remote and idyllic setting serious work is going on all the time. The peaceful lake of Ess See lies in the heart of the countryside and looks more like a holiday paradise than the headquarters of a scientific institute. Houses and laboratories are situated close to the shores of the lake and the zoologists spend much of their time out of doors. Sunburnt men walk without undue haste along footpaths. A young lady, surrounded by a flock of black and yellow ducklings, sits talking to them and, when she gets up, they totter along behind her like a pack of dogs at heel. This unusual cavalcade is met by another young lady who has a fur draped round her neck: a tame mongoose having its morning outing in this agreeable manner. There is a rustle overhead and a young jackdaw lands elegantly on the head of a man as he walks by.

A little farther on there is a remarkably bright coloured cock strutting about a meadow in the sunshine. A small metal box, the size of a matchbox, gleams between the feathers on his back. The cock suddenly stops, has a good stretch and then lowers himself into the grass and apparently falls fast asleep — all this in broad daylight. After a short while he gets up again, shakes his feathers and resumes his strutting as though a nap in the sun were the most natural thing in the life of a cock.

Several men and women, all wearing white smocks, emerge from a house in the background. They approach the cock quietly and one of the women throws down a handful of crumbs. The cock starts to peck at them and she picks him up. There is no fuss and it is obvious that he is accustomed to being handled. Then one of the men gently removes some strips of sticking plaster from the cock's feathers and takes away the metal box. The cock is released, he finishes pecking at the crumbs and then walks away while the men have a chat.

The scene is slightly odd but it is just another piece of research. The people in smocks are zoologists, physiologists and physicists and they have only one aim: to find out what animals do and *why* they do it. The handsome cock is one of the key figures in their experiments. The research workers are concerned with many problems but in this particular case they want to find out which regions of a fowl's brain send out the nerve impulses which give rise to various kinds of behaviour. Which nerve centre, for instance, must be stimulated so that the cock will become aggressive, thereby making the hen warn her chicks of a poten= tial danger? To find out the answer to this question, it was essential to perform a small and painless brain operation. When the cock was very young a small circular piece was removed under anaesthetic from the roof of the skull. People who are opposed to operations on experimental animals will find it hard to believe that the cock did not suffer; but it remained normally active and gave no indication of having undergone any pain. The opening was made near the comb and a small plastic cylinder was inserted; electrodes, in the shape of fine silver wires, were then passed through the cylinder into the brain. Very low volts of 0.1 to 0.5 could now be sent along the wire into the brain of the cock, thus stimulating the nerves leading to the motor cortex — that part of the brain which controls move= ment.

The layman finds it a somewhat uncanny experience to be present while experiments of this nature are being performed. A young technical assistant hangs a sign on the door of the laboratory: "Experiment in progress. Do not disturb." There is complete silence in the laboratory. Scientists squat behind their apparatus with their hands ready to turn knobs and switches. There is a low hum from the oscilloscope tube and a thin green band quivers across the screen and changes into sharp peaks or low undulations, according to the nature of the bird's calls received from a microphone. Ciné film and still photographs make a record of the experiment.

The cock stands on a high circular table in front of the observation window. Thin wires lead directly from the ceiling to the animal's head. An electric current can be passed along them at will. A female assistant stands beside the cock. She looks at her colleague behind the screen: "Shall I give it one more turn?" she asks. "Yes, one more." Quietly and gently she takes hold of the bird's head and grips one of the four tiny screws which protrude from the plastic cylinder near the cock's comb; with deft fingers she gives it a single turn. The silver electrodes drive a fraction of a millimetre deeper between the nerve fibres leading to the motor cortex of the cock's brain. The cock stands perfectly still, he feels no pain and accepts it all with the equanimity of one who is familiar with the proceedings. "Ready?" "Yes, ready." "Switch on!" A switch clicks.

Then the cock gives an extraordinary performance which at first sight appears to be quite inexplicable. He stands on the table, apparently quite content; he then stretches and treads restlessly on the same spot; next he starts to circle on the table, slowly at first and then faster, as though following someone; at the edge of the table he suddenly stops, makes a bow and spreads his right wing, fanning the feathers so that they scrape audibly along the surface of the table by his foot. There was no hen in the laboratory but through the electrical stimulation of his brain the cock was responding to an imaginary hen.

A cock giving his courtship display to order: a weird performance because the animal involuntarily does something demanded of it by man. It cannot avoid reacting to the stimuli received through the wires. Experiments in which the responses of a fowl are invoked by electrical stimuli were originated by the late Professor Erich von Holst. Before his untimely death he was able to comment on his investigations in the following terms:

Responses may be classified into simple movements and more complex activities. Among the simple movements are, for instance, sitting down, stand= ing up, feather preening, removal of parasites, looking around on the alert (sometimes accompanied by alarm call), looking into the distance (sometimes accompanied by aerial=warning call), courtship movement of scratching the ground, and orientation movements. Complex activities include: searching for food and eating what is found, searching for water and drinking, flight from ground predator, flight from aerial predator, and the process of falling asleep.

Such laboratory experiments have shown that man can induce certain animals to behave in a way which is apparently "determined" by the animal itself. But would normal members of the same species understand it when this artificially produced behaviour was shown? The answer to this question cannot be found under laboratory conditions because the cock must be allowed to move freely and associate with other fowls in the fresh air. It was obvious that, under such conditions, the cock could not be attached to wires and that a technique for stimulating it must be found which would avoid their use. For years the physicists in Professor Holst's department tried to find some method of remote control which was practical. They eventually found it.

A fifteen=foot high pole was placed in the experimental paddock. Small trans= mitting antennae were suspended from it and they sent out decimeter waves to the ground in much the same way as water pours through the rose of a watering can. The impulses from the antennae were picked up by a miniature receiver which was placed on the back of the cock; and the receiver passed on the pulses through the plastic cylinder to the cock's brain. However, before the first field experiment was conducted, the scientists did further laboratory tests to establish which areas in the brain would produce clearcut reactions when stimulated. One of the problems not yet solved is the difficulty of determining precisely, in advance, how far the tips of the wires will reach. The thread=like nerve fibres have highly differentiated functions and they lie so close together in the brain that only a tiny fraction of a turn, in one of the hand=operated screws, may carry the stimulating electrode from, say, the sleep nerve fibre to the path concerned with escape. And so the exciting search into the cock's brain continued in the laboratory. Two remarkable discoveries were made: it was found that there were two different areas in the brain which acted as warning centres. An electrode in one of them stimulated the cock to give the alarm against a ground predator, whereas in the other area the electrode stimulated the alarm against aerial predators.

Before the start of the field experiment the screws in the cylinder were fixed in position with quick=setting glue; if the screws shift an infinitesimal amount the success of the whole experiment would be jeopardized. The small receiver was fastened into the feathers on the cock's back by means of sticking=plaster. Thin wires connected it with the electrodes in the cock's brain. The bird was then put into the experimental paddock which was surrounded by wire=netting. The tips of the receiving antennae peeped out from the feathers, ready to receive the radio waves from the gallows above. The cock was familiar with the wire=netting enclosure, as this was his territory when he was not being used by the scientists. Here he led a normal life with his hens, fought with rivals, mated, gave warning calls to his hens and behaved as a typical cock in a hen run. The success of the experiment depended on the assumption that the hens would listen, in the normal way, to the voice of their master the cock. Assuming that they regarded him as their normal "leader", would they also react to him if he gave them an order which was apparently crazy?

The field experiment started with the hens' being released in the wire=netting enclosure. The assistants fed them to encourage them to settle down. The cock was then put with them and, as the hens pecked quietly at the food, he stood by, looking every inch their master. The scene was completely peaceful; there were no signs of unrest.

This was the moment for which the scientists had waited. They switched on the transmitter, keeping the voltage low at first and then gradually increasing the current to approximately 0.5 volts. The receiver on the cock's back started to pass on the impulses and electrical stimuli trickled into the bird's brain. The cock stretched and gazed into the distance over his peacefully pecking flock; then he started to give his alarm call. The hens paid attention. His warning cackles became louder and developed into a shrieking alarm call: he was giving the typical alarm call for the approach of a ground predator, such as a fox. The hens looked frightened, stretched their necks and peered in all directions. They could not see a predator, but if their cock gave the alarm it was best to pay heed. Hens rely a great deal on their cock; he is not only a tyrant but also a sentinel guarding their safety. The cock suddenly ran away from the imaginary predator, cackling loudly, and the hens scattered automatically. Although there was no predator in sight they all took evasive action. It was as though a fox had suddenly appeared in their midst. As the cock continued to give the alarm call, running hither and thither, the hens made for the side of the experimental paddock, pressing against the wire nearest to the hen=house, the safest refuge in the life of a hen. The scientists switched off the current and everything quietened down. The cock reacted immediately, shook his feathers and settled down. The hens were slower to respond to this sudden change and it was some time before they returned to normal.

In the second experiment the nerves leading to the area concerned with aerial predators were stimulated. The cock stretched his neck up into the air and gave a continuous warning cackle: "Look out! Air attack!" He ducked down into the grass, screaming in a high descant: this is the typical warning movement and alarm call for an aerial predator. The hens screamed and ducked down like the cock, apparently "frozen" to the ground.

The experiments were finished. The research team now knew that behaviour patterns provoked by artificially stimulating the appropriate nerve fibres are accepted in normal surroundings and are reacted to in the proper way. Erich von Holst lived long enough to hear the results of these early experiments. Greater things lay ahead, because his work was now at a point where it was beginning to cast doubts on the validity of Pavlov's classical theory of reflexes.

CHAPTER 29

They Talk to Eggs

THE BOAT GLIDED across the lake at Seewiesen as I shipped my oars, the water moving gently under the keel and the boat drifting forwards. It was essential to behave quietly on Ess See in order not to disturb the geese which were nesting. It was a man=made breeding site and stakes with nest boxes attached had been driven into the lake. The boxes had lids which gave easy access to the eggs when examining the nests.

I was in the middle of the breeding area and at nest 16A, just in front of me, one of the members of the Institute staff was at work. A young lady in a boat was being attacked by a grey gander, which made a huge bow=wave as it rushed at the boat only to turn aside at the last moment. The girl made the boat fast to the stake and raised the lid of the nesting=box. She wore no gloves and put her hands right into the nest. There was a scream of protest from the grey goose, who pecked at her. She removed an egg and, as far as I could see, she spoke to the egg and then held it up to her ear. She listened . . . .

As my boat drifted up to 16A I asked her what she was doing.

"Nest examination," she replied, "I am talking to the egg because I want to see whether the unhatched gosling is alive. Listen, it's answering." I took the egg from her and placed my ear against the warm shell. I could just hear a low "wi=wi=wi — wi=wi=wi", which was the same sound as the young assistant had made when she talked to the egg. She explained to me that she was removing some of the eggs from the nest in order to put them in an incubator for the last few days before hatching. The idea was to rear chicks which would never have seen their real goose=mother and which would, therefore, be suitable for imprint=ing.

The subject of imprinting was the reason for my paying yet another visit to the Max Planck Institute. The young lady in the boat was one of the scientific assistants of Professor Konrad Lorenz, who is known to the public as the man who speaks to beasts, birds and fish and who has been working on the problems of imprinting for many years. Research in this field covers a very wide area and is concerned with what is inborn and what has to be learnt. To differentiate between these two, "Kaspar=Hauser" animals are reared — that is, animals which first see the light of day in isolation from members of their own species. Under these conditions such animals can best reveal those characteristics which are inborn. The young of some animals when reared in isolation from their natural parents attach themselves to anyone who looks after them during the sensitive or labile period, as it is termed at Seewiesen. In geese and ducks this lasts for a few hours after hatching. During this critical time the young animal can become imprinted on a human being, or it can even become imprinted visually on an inanimate object or acoustically on a sound. There is an inborn tendency in many young animals to run after or follow their mother; so, whatever they associate with during this critical period becomes "Mother" to them. Ducklings or goslings, for instance, will accept all manner of things as a "mother", they merely have to learn the physical attributes of this substitute parent. The study of these problems has yielded some fantastic results, and it leads to situations which never occur in everyday life.

Animals imprinted on humans can become quite a nuisance. One evening I was rung up by my old friend Dr Theodor Haltenorth, Director of the Mammal Department of the Bavarian State Zoological Collection.

"I want to ask a favour," he said. "I know you often drive out to Seewiesen; next time you go, could you possibly call in here and relieve me of my tormentor? I cannot stand it any longer, it never leaves me alone. It sits under the desk in my office and if I get up it runs after me. And if I leave it alone — as one must on occasions — it complains so loudly that it would melt the stoniest heart; my colleagues think that I am ill=treating it. I cannot leave it in the office, I have to take it home with me and it insists on getting into bed with me. It wakes at four each morning, as punctual as an alarm clock, and wants to talk to me. You simply must get me out of this. Will you take it to Seewiesen?"

"Of course I will," I replied, "but I don't think they welcome cats there."

Dr Haltenorth laughed at the other end of the line: "What do you think my tormentor really is?" he asked.

"If it isn't a cat," I replied, "what is it then?"

"You come and see for yourself."

I then became a little anxious and thought of all the possible quadrupeds. After all, Dr Haltenorth worked in the Mammal Department; it might even be a mongoose. But I need not have worried. Eventually I drove to Schloss Nymphenburg and Dr Haltenorth met me in a corridor flanked by exhibits of gaping crocodiles.

"Where is your mysterious animal?" I asked, "I hope you have got a travelling cage for it."

"Everything is organized, just look here," he said, pointing to his feet.

He certainly took me by surprise. Squatting down by his shoes was a very small duckling.

Mother is made of wood: a fantastic looking idyll at the Max Planck Institute of Behaviour Physiology: the wooden mother duck is part of an experiment to determine the time taken by duck=lings to become imprinted. Seconds after they hatched out in an incubator, the ducklings followed the wooden duck to the bath as though it were their natural mother.

Talking to an egg: this dialogue is part of a control check on nests containing eggs laid by wild geese on the Ess See which is used by research workers from Seewiesen. A short time before hatch=ing, the chick will react to the mother goose's "wi=wi=wi" and will give an audible reply.

(Right) Cock love to order: a stimulatory current passes through the finest silver electrodes to the nerve centre which controls courtship and the laboratory cock performs the most beautiful "foot=scratching" movements, just as he would when standing in front of a desired hen in the farmyard.

An apparently weird but entirely painless experiment in the laboratory: the cock stands on the lab. table and while beating his wings he suddenly falls asleep — the stimulatory current has reached the sleep centre in the brain. Film cameras and tape recorders make a continuous record of all movements and sounds. What purpose does all this serve?

The behaviour physiologists want to know the precise location in a fowl's brain of the regions which stimulate its drives. Is Pavlov's theory of reflexes still valid? The open=air experiment showed that hens understand the instructions of a radio=directed cock and react correctly to them (see p. 292).

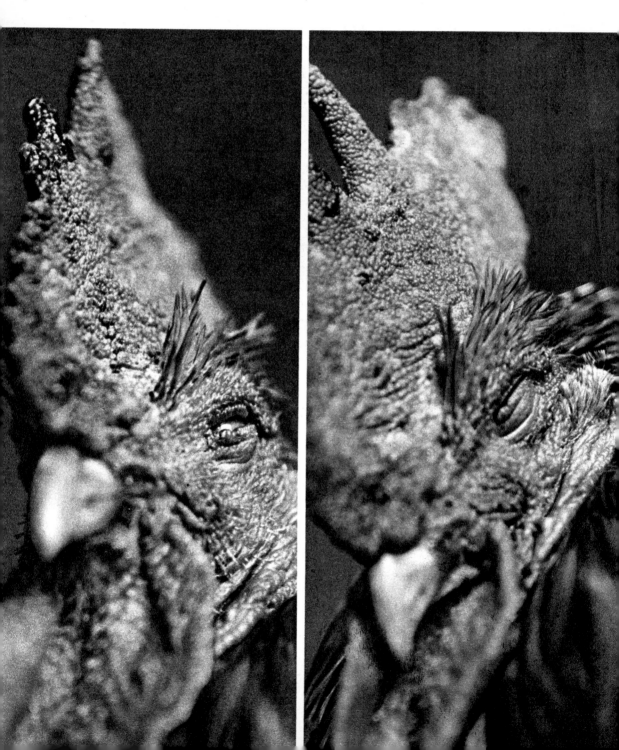

"Duncie" cannot crack nuts. In a laboratory with humans to help he is all right, but in the wild he would not have survived.

Competent squirrels attack nut=shells in various ways: the really efficient make only two grooves running the length of the fibres; this is sufficient to get at the kernel.

Another technique works equally well: first, several short grooves are made, running to the tip of the nut; then the outer casing is crushed by the small teeth.

This specialist seems to have the most labour=saving method of all: he splits the nut open with three or four notches set like a cogwheel.

This is typical of the begin= ner who works without a system. Dr Eibl=Eibesfeldt investigated the behaviour of the squirrel and collected these revealing nut=shells.

It never occurs to the duckling that the chick really does not want to go into the water and the duckling keeps on calling to it. These youngsters are growing up together as part of Dr Schutz's research programme. He wants to imprint the male jungle-fowl on the duckling. When the young jungle-fowl grew up into a proud cock it showed quite clearly that it thought it really was a duck (right).

One day when the ducks were frightened they flew right out into the lake. The "jungle-fowl duck" was caught up in the excitement of the flight and landed in the water. He managed to reach the shore by swimming.

Five wild goslings swim after the man because they believe he is their mother. The man in the water whom they are following is Professor Konrad Lorenz, well known for his work on the behaviour of wild geese. He had imprinted the goslings on himself.

Toads are clever animals.

Dr Eibl=Eibesfeldt shows by a simple experiment how clever toads are. When they catch prey, toads have an inborn snapping reaction which is released by a special stimulus: every object within a certain size range which moves is snapped at. They will even take pebbles, small leaves, feathers and so on. On the other hand, no notice is taken of motionless prey: hence the well= known death=feigning reflex of many insects.

Toads learn quickly. As they hunt anything which moves they must learn immediately to differ=
entiate. Dr Eibl placed dead mealworms and other non=mobile, edible objects in front of the
toad, and these offerings remained untouched. But when a matchstick on a thread was drawn
along a line between the animal and the dead mealworms, it was immediately snapped up and spat
out again in a flash. The same experiment was repeated, but the toad did not make the same mistake
again. It hastily left the experimental plot.

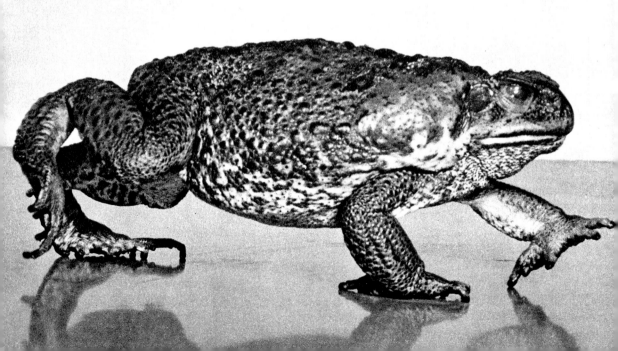

The marvel of birth. The electronic flash went off to record a process which is repeated day in, day out but which never seems an everyday event. An elongated little sac lies pale and shining beneath the dachshund bitch. Something moves within the transparent covering; the newly born wants to burst its covering. The mother assists by biting open the amnion and she severs the umbilical cord. Schnitzi's third puppy lies naked and free: its blind brother and sister sniff at the latest member of the litter.

Four little dachshund puppies find their own way to the sources of nourishment. They cannot see until they are twelve days old and no one has told them where they can get nourishment. Instinct guides them to the right place. The last puppy has only just been born. As each one arrives, the bitch uses her tongue to massage and dry it until it squeaks. One can tell the order in which they were born — from left to right — by the dryness of their coats.

"Allow me to present Agatha," he said.

Agatha was a wild mallard. Some children had found the duckling abandoned on the river Isar and they said it was on its own, calling plaintively. Agatha must have been a few days old when they found her. Although Dr Haltenorth did not reckon to look after birds, he agreed to look after the young duckling, which promptly accepted him as "mother". So the attractive Agatha developed into a tormentor. She sat quite fearlessly between Dr Haltenorth's shoes and preened, oblivious of the fact that her "mother" had more important matters which required his attention. The good man had certainly given me an exagger= ated impression of the nature of his tormentor in an effort to be rid of her, but I could see that a duck was scarcely an appropriate companion for him in his office.

Agatha was accustomed to being transported in a clothes basket from the house to the office and Dr Haltenorth suggested that I simply put her in the basket beside me in the car. He said that he always did this. With a sigh of relief, he thanked me, wished me a good journey and disappeared rapidly. Funny people, these zoologists, I thought. I looked down at Agatha sitting demurely in her bas= ket beside me and wondered if I should take her home with me. I had not gone far before I changed my mind. By the time I turned the first corner Agatha was sitting on my lap. I put on the brakes and came to a halt: "How did you get there?" She looked up at me, her liquid eyes full of trust, her head on one side. My lap suited her and she started preening. No female, however small, should sit on a man's lap when he is driving and I put her back in the basket. At the next crossroads there was another "plonk" — Agatha had been waddling around in her basket and it had fallen off the seat. By this time I had had enough and decided that she had better go in the boot. This turned out to be a mistake. Before I had driven a few yards she was calling in a shrill, heart=rending way and, as I drew up at some traffic lights, people stopped and stared. They looked angrily at me and obviously thought I was one of those people who are cruel to animals. An old man came up to the car window but fortunately the lights changed. Agatha continued to protest loudly and I now understood what Dr Haltenorth suffered. I pulled up again and transferred Agatha to the front of the car, putting her down on the floor. I scolded her so much that she was quiet but this peace did not last long and she soon resumed her cries. She stopped when I talked to her but started up again as soon as I was silent. It ended with my talking practically non=stop for the 25 miles to Seewiesen. Agatha was a typical example of imprinting on humans. The children on the Isar had appeared so early in Agatha's life that she became accustomed to accepting humans as her "mother".

After the first meal the bitch takes her puppies in hand again and one after the other they are all cleaned with her nose and tongue. This new brood of small impudent puppies will grow up and, specially selected for the purpose, they will contribute to our understanding of animals.

At Seewiesen I had great difficulty in getting rid of Agatha. She had become so used to my voice on the journey that she now followed me about the Institute's grounds in the same way that she had accompanied Dr Haltenorth in the Zoolo=gical Museum. Fortunately one of the assistants, a young lady named Renate, was willing to take over the time=consuming business of rearing Agatha. We spent a morning by a pond, intending to give Agatha a bath. The little duckling never let me out of her sight. As long as I sat on the bank all went well, but the moment I stood up she came out of the water. I kept completely silent and Renate spoke continuously to Agatha. By mid=day Agatha had become accustomed to Renate.

I met Renate by the lake a few days later. She told me of sleepless nights during which she had made strenuous efforts to persuade Agatha that it was not usual for a duck to sleep in a human bed. Agatha now slept in a basket under the bed but, wherever Renate went, Agatha went too. The duckling was always with her, in her arms, under her pullover, waddling behind her and so on. It takes several weeks for wild ducklings to outgrow the attachment to their mothers; the unnatural bond between Agatha and the human would be similarly loosened and one day it might even be completely severed. There were a lot of "Agathas" running about at Seewiesen that spring.

A motor=horn suddenly tooted behind me. I stepped to one side and turned round to see Professor Lorenz laughing at me. A sunburnt figure in shorts, he was holding a long bamboo pole which he pushed along in front of him. At the end of the pole there was a grey goose made of cardboard which rolled along. The sound of the horn came from inside the cardboard goose. A real young grey goose stood waiting by the cardboard model. When the Professor pushed, the model trundled along, accompanied by the real goose; the latter was imprinted on the model and Professor Lorenz was taking them for a walk by the lake. It was a remarkable sight.

The Professor explained the purpose of this unusual set=up. "The dummy need not be in the form of a goose," he said, "any shape will do. The animal merely has to get to know it during the critical period. To prove his point, he picked up another long bamboo pole with a white cube running on wheels at the end of it. A young snow goose was resting beside it. He pressed a button in the handle of the pole: a buzzer sounded and the snow goose immediately got up. The Pro=fessor walked on with the wild snow goose following; the white cube which made a sound like a buzzer was its "mother".

The Professor first led the snow goose to the side of the lake and then went back for the dummy grey goose with its grey gosling. The live birds would not go into the water until the dummies on the long poles were held in front of them over the surface of the water. It was a warm day and the Professor went for a swim but the two imprinted geese did not follow him as they were only interested in their "mothers". However, there were five other wild goslings standing on the bank in a separate group from the other goose families and, as soon as these

goslings saw the man swimming, they went into the water in line=ahead for=
mation and paddled as fast as they could after the Professor. He saw the formation
and called out to them: "Komm, komm, komm." There was no need for him to
use goose language as all five were imprinted on his voice, his figure and his
movements. For them the "Komm=komm=komm" call was the call of their "mother".
They had no ties with members of their own species and animals, at present, were
stranger to them than humans. Later on the picture would change and the human
element would gradually fade out.

Professor Lorenz swam back to the shore, followed closely by the five goslings.
While he dried himself the youngsters preened themselves. These ducklings preen,
wash, feed and swim in line=ahead formation although no one has taught them
how to do so. They go to sleep trying to tuck their heads under their wings, even
though the tiny wing stumps, bearing down feathers only, could never cover
their beaks. How do they know all this and who tells them what is necessary for
survival? The embryo in the egg already has the answer in its blood when it calls
"Wi, wi, wi"; this is inborn. And the gosling has scarcely hatched before it starts
to feed. At first it pecks at everything. In this case it learns from experience what
tastes good; it learns, for instance, the difference between chips of wood and grains
of corn.

I walked a little way with the Professor along the shores of the lake to the
goose house. It is always an unforgettable experience to be with him amongst
hundreds of wildfowl and each time I feel that I have never been so close to
wildlife. He will suddenly lay his hand on the arm of a visitor and say: "You see
that greylag family, the one with the four goslings? The parents have just said
that they want to go and bathe." One looks sceptically at his weatherbeaten face
and then back at the geese. True enough: the family makes off in the direction
of the water and they are soon paddling across the lake in line formation with
Father in the lead, the four youngsters in between, and Mother bringing up
the rear.

The visitor's tour continues. "Keep your eye on the Canada geese, they have
just agreed to go off to feed." No sooner said than done, it happens exactly as
predicted. The next surprise follows quickly, when the Professor takes his pipe
out of his mouth and points to one of the Canada geese standing in the distance
where the others went to graze. "That one is Constance; she will soon be over
to greet me, she has just said so." And he is quite right. Constance comes over to
greet her master, her long neck extended as she bows to him. "She is called Con=
stance because she once made the journey to the Bodensee," he explains. "She is
quite free to come and go but when she had had enough of Lake Constance she
came back again." I want to know how he can be certain that this goose had
actually been to Lake Constance. "It is quite simple. All our free=flying birds are
ringed and at Constance the Ess See ring was recognized. I could have arranged
for her to be caught but I preferred to let her decide for herself. It must have been
quite a powerful pull to bring her all this way back."

Professor Lorenz is second to none in his knowledge of "goose talk". He has been studying the social life of geese and the behaviour patterns of wild duck for decades. Moreover, he devotes his whole life to waterfowl. At Ess See he and his colleagues observe how animals behave and try to investigate why they do one thing and not another. The Professor and his ducks and geese are now as well known in the study of animal behaviour as T. H. Morgan's fruit=flies in the study of genetics.

Dr Schutz, a colleague of Professor Lorenz, built a so=called imprinting machine to get the "purest" form of imprinting and also to determine as precisely as pos= sible the period of imprinting. The machine consisted of a plywood duck which circled in a course rather similar to a circus arena. It hung from an electrically driven gibbet which allowed it to circulate forwards or backwards. The plywood duck "quacked" by means of a loudspeaker which reproduced a recording of a mallard mother's call. The ducklings obeyed the orders of the dummy "mother". They ran backwards and forwards as the dummy altered direction. The dummy led them to and from the water for a bath. When it halted, the ducklings took a rest and preened themselves in the shade cast by the dummy. Although their mother was only made out of wood they behaved as though everything was in order. Dr Schutz established that the "sensitive period" in the life of a small duckling starts when it is approximately seventeen hours old and may last up to three days. Imprinting is possible only during this period. According to the most recent results of Dr Schutz's work, the actual imprinting may be accomplished in seconds.

The possibilities of imprinting are numerous and varied; they are not restricted to the relation of animal to man or of animal to dummy. Given a suitable part= ner, an animal may be imprinted on another animal; in this case the animals "belong" to each other irrespective of their biological relationship. There are many fables and legends concerning animals of different species living together; these are surely based on observations of imprinted animals.

There is a fairy=tale atmosphere at Seewiesen and, if I had not known that I was on the solid ground of a scientific institution, I would not have believed what I saw. I have already mentioned Dr Nicolai's doves in an earlier chapter. After a long period of observation at the nest I often used to relax near the lake; sitting on an old nestbox just to the right of the doves, I would watch the water= fowl on the lake. There was a marvellous jungle cock who used to go around with the ducks. Incidentally, all our varieties of domestic fowls come from original stock of junglefowl from Java. My jungle cock obviously had something to do with the ducks: it took a siesta with them under the bushes and went foraging with them; it gave marvellous courtship displays of foot=scratching before many of the ducks without receiving any recognition, and as soon as the flotilla of ducks went out on to the lake it often accompanied them until the water came up to its belly. It was an incredible sight. It stood in the lake, long tail=feathers trailing in the water, waiting for its ducks to return home. The highspot of all this, as far as I was concerned, occurred one day at noon. For some reason or other the ducks showed signs of alarm: they quacked anxiously and, as always in such situations, they fled into the water. Infected by the general alarm and flight, the brightly coloured little cock went with them as though drawn by a magnet. Calling frantically, it fluttered over the shore and towered up, flying over the heads of the ducks out above the lake and then landed in the water. I sprang up with my camera ready. Surely the cock would drown — its plumage was not waterproof like that of the ducks. On the contrary: it turned in an elegant curve and came swimming back to the shore with tail=feathers trailing behind. It must have thought it really was a duck.

Everything could be explained by the fact that, shortly after the jungle cock was hatched, Dr Schutz reared it with the mallard ducklings. The junglefowl was imprinted on ducks.

On one occasion Professor Lorenz said to me: "I could even give wild goslings a fox as "mother", if only I could trust the fox not to eat them. . . ."

CHAPTER 30

Learn or Perish

DR IRENAEUS EIBL=EIBESFELDT is one of Professor Lorenz's scientific assistants at the Max Planck Institute at Seewiesen. He belongs to the generation of young zoologists whose research into behaviour is internationally known. One of his many interests is the conservation of animal life in the Galapagos Islands. With the support of Unesco, several expeditions were organized to these islands in the Pacific Ocean whose rich and interesting fauna are due to their long iso= lation from the rest of the animal world. The first biological research station for the Galapagos Islands was founded by Dr Eibl=Eibesfeldt on one of the islands in the archipelago.

Dr Eibl is frequently away from Seewiesen when I call. We have known each other for a long time and I have ceased to be surprised at not finding him there. In the course of our acquaintance we have come to an arrangement by which, in his absence, I am allowed free access to his animals, both in the laboratory and in the outside paddocks. If I need anything special I refer to Anna, Dr Eibl's faithful assistant. On one of my visits to Seewiesen I went into the laboratory and found Dr Eibl's desk deserted as usual. Behind it, on the right=hand side, was a Galapagos finch. It was stabbing with a needle=like splinter at a branch of worm= eaten wood and fishing out grubs with it. This bird does not have a woodpecker's long tongue for getting prey out of cracks and crevices and has to make use of a tool or starve. As Eibl says, the Galapagos finch is an outstanding example of a bird that uses tools.

Immediately behind the desk, members of a family of tree=shrews were having a romp. The tree=shrews are Asiatic insectivorous ancestors of apes and monkeys. In a vivarium to the left were three large toads and two Galapagos iguanas and these all stared fixedly at me. I have known these animals longer than their master, because when I first visited the Institute Dr Eibl was on an expedition to the Indian Ocean. In front of the desk there was a large indoor cage containing squirrels and agoutis. Agoutis have interested me ever since I saw them on my first visit to the Institute after the war, when it was in temporary quarters at Buldern in Westphalia. Agoutis are long=legged rodents. They live in the rain= forests of Central and South America and sometimes have a golden sheen. Eibl's agoutis were dark brown with a wonderful greenish patina. These creatures are exceedingly lively and alert; they have long claws and, when feeding, sit on their haunches and convey the food to their mouths with their front paws in much the same way as a squirrel. I never tire of watching them. I had intended to do some work with the squirrels but I became absorbed by the agoutis. Anna had pointed out one which was only twenty=four hours old and as I watched I suddenly realized that the baby agouti was receiving some very rough treatment from the others. It went to sniff an adult, approaching in quite a friendly way, but the adult sat on its haunches, lifted its front paws and drummed the bewildered baby. The baby fled, pursued by the scolding adult, and ran up to a second adult, which was feeding; it pushed under this animal, as though seeking shelter. I assumed that the second adult was the baby's mother but the little creature quickly re= emerged and ran away as fast as its little legs could carry it; this adult appeared to be totally unimpressed and went on feeding — which did not strike me as very mater= nal. The baby continued its wanderings and it suddenly dawned on me that it had become separated from its mother. It then trotted up to a third adult and I thought that this one must surely be its mother: the baby ran between the adult's forelegs as though making straight for the milk source but the "mother" made herself very tall, by stiffening her hind legs, and the baby ran straight down the tunnel and out the other end. This was obviously not its mother either. The little one started to cry and ran up to yet another. This time it had the misfortune to approach a half=grown agouti which responded by drumming the baby's head. The baby screamed and another adult came galloping across; it butted the half=grown agouti and then offered the baby its flank. At last the baby was reunited with its mother.

A few days later I was talking to Dr Eibl and he gave me the explanation of the "unfriendly" behaviour of the agouti society. An agouti is born with hair and it can see. It can run immediately after birth and it possesses an innate "following" reaction: all the young animals run after other members of the same species but, as these animals live in groups, it naturally happens that the young ones run up to strange males and females; when this happens the adults repel the youngsters by drumming them with their forelegs — but they never bite them. Through this "punishment" the youngster learns to avoid strange animals and to seek only its mother. The "following" reaction is inborn but the young animal has to be shown whom to follow. Nature has endowed her children with the ability to learn and she demands that they use this ability; if they fail to do so, they fail to survive.

Dr Eibl's laboratory has a wide programme of research into this special prob= lem. He showed me his big toads and let me see a simple experiment which proved that toads learn quickly to distinguish between edible and inedible prey, even when the latter corresponds in appearance with the former. Toads have an inborn snapping reaction when catching prey. This is released by a simple key= stimulus. They will snap at every moving object within a certain size range; this includes such objects as stones, leaves, and small feathers, providing they are made to move. On the other hand, non=moving objects, even if they are prey animals, will be disregarded if they sit motionless. The death=feigning reflex of many insects is significant, seen in this context.

Dr Eibl gave me a private demonstration. He told me that a toad quickly learns to avoid unpalatable prey. For example toads only need to be stung once or twice by a wasp to leave wasps completely alone even when they are moving, for the striking appearance of a wasp is easily recognized by a toad. Dr Eibl offered his experimental toad two heaps, one consisting of dead mealworms and the other of live mealworms. The toad appeared not to notice the dead ones and caught the live ones instantly. We then tied a small white feather to a thread and Dr Eibl jerked it along between the toad and the mealworms. I was surprised by the reaction of the toad: it looked at the object but in no way reacted to the inborn releasing stimulus — on the contrary, it stood up and withdrew from the test area with long strides. According to Eibl's previous statement to me, the toad should have snapped at it. Why did it not do so? The answer was quite simple: this toad knew the feather from a previous experiment; Dr Eibl remembered that it had already been tested with a feather. We then tried the same experiment with trouser but= tons and metal screws and once again our toad did not fancy them, it knew better. It was already an aged toad and had learnt a lot in its life. It did not fall into any of our traps. Possibly it saw the thread but there was no way of telling.

We took another toad and tied a match to a thread. The experiment followed the same course as before. First, the second toad was put in front of the meal= worms, dead and living; next, a match was jerked along. This time the evidence was quite plain: the toad instantly pounced on the matchstick with its front legs and seized it with its sticky tongue; it did not taste it at all but flung it out of its mouth. The toad looked so disgusted and so serious about it all that it was quite comical. It ignored a second test with the match, even when we let a dragonfly flit about over the piece of wood.

When Dr Eibl introduced me to his next animal it was peeping out of a circular hole in a box which hung from the wire=netting surrounding the agouti paddock. The box, which looked rather like a nest=box for starlings, was the sleeping quarters of an attractive little red squirrel named Duncie. At first sight, Duncie was indistinguishable in appearance from thousands of other red squirrels which live wild in the forests of Europe. But Duncie's natural endowment as far as in= telligence was concerned made it easy to distinguish him from other members of his species. Unfortunately Duncie was not mentally equipped to survive because he was too stupid to know how to open a nut, an essential operation in the life of a squirrel. To demonstrate this Dr Eibl filled a bowl with uncracked hazel=nuts and placed the bowl on a feeding board which hung on the wire=netting at the same height as Duncie's sleeping box. The inquisitive squirrel came out imme= diately and pushed his head in amongst the nuts so that they rolled about and toppled off the board; he then turned away and pressed himself into the corner. He had not touched a single nut with his paws. Duncie knew nothing about ker=

nels inside shells and if he had been out in the wood in a hazel tree, surrounded by nuts, he would still have starved. Nature makes short shrift of ignoramuses. Duncie might have been able to last a summer on soft fruit, but even if he had the inborn drive to store supplies of nuts for the winter, he would perish without the knowledge of how to deal with the contents of his larder.

The ill=equipped Duncie had the indescribable luck to be born one of Dr Eibl's experimental animals. Help was at hand. As the squirrel sulked in the corner Anna made a noise with some nutcrackers and Duncie at once came forward. He could scarcely wait until the first nut was cracked and his claws fingered the nutcrackers. He liked hazel=nuts very much when they were freed from the shell.

Duncie's lack of ability was in sharp contrast to the picture presented by the average squirrel. Our image of a squirrel is of an agile, deft creature which appears to be clever enough to make provision for the future by hoarding food. But do squirrels really have insight? Dr Eibl tried to unravel this problem for me.

He told me that he had reared squirrels in wire cages, feeding them only on fluids and broth so that they could not learn how to carry objects or bury them. When they were fully grown he then tested them by offering them nuts to see if they showed any inclination to bury food. After the squirrels had eaten suffi= cient to satisfy their immediate appetite, they began to look for somewhere to bury them even though they could never have seen food buried before. They did not know why but they were driven by a blind urge to behave in this particular way and they began to scrape the solid floor in a corner of the room: they placed the nuts in a heap and pushed at them with their noses and then made filling=in motions in the air, although they had not been able to dig a hole. Dr Eibl said that the whole sequence of behaviour patterns was inborn. Squirrels do not have to learn how to hide nuts as a food store, they are naturally endowed with this pattern of behaviour.

We returned to the subject of why Duncie was unable to open nuts and Dr Eibl produced the next bit of evidence: many small bags, each containing a number of nut shells. When I watch squirrels eating nuts I am full of admiration for the way in which they deal with them. But as a scientific observer Dr Eibl naturally observes every detail, and when a squirrel eats a nut he examines the shell that the squirrel drops. He emptied each bag into a separate pile on his desk. To me they appeared to be just discarded, empty shells, but to the scientist each one told a story.

The first bit of evidence consisted of nuts dropped by beginners. The shells showed distinctly how the nut was turned round and round until finally the shell split. The marks made by the sharp incisors were indiscriminate. But, with ex= perience, the squirrels learn not to work against the grain but to follow the fibres. The young squirrel soon learns to apply its energy sparingly in order to achieve its aim of getting at the kernel. On the basis of experience each one builds up favourite techniques. Some gnaw a square piece out of the apex, many furrows run up to the apex; others get at the kernel in much the same way except that they circle the apex with four incisions shaped like a cogwheel, breaking the kernel out; the most elegant, in my opinion, were the type which were neatly bisected, following the grain from apex to base in the same way as we would slice an apple in half.

The squirrel is endowed with the ability to gnaw with its teeth. Teeth are virtually the tools of a squirrel and it has to learn how to use them efficiently. Dr Eibl said that it would not be expedient for a squirrel to have an inborn tech=nique for opening hazel=nuts because there are many kinds of nuts and fruit stones, each requiring its own technique. It would be quite impossible for an ani=mal to have a nerve centre sufficiently complex to give innate responses to such a wide variety of shells.

CHAPTER 31

The Cock Who Thought He Was a Pug

I HAVE ALREADY mentioned the natural phenomenon known as the "follow=ing" reaction by which an animal runs after another. This is by no means limited to the examples I have described. Following responses take place all over the world and are not restricted to animals. Without them there would be no meeting together and no social life. This is self=evident; but we take normal behaviour for granted and our sense of wonder tends to be aroused only by the exception to the rule. The chance association of members of different species immediately attracts attention and the social life of an animal which does not fit into its own society is always of interest.

I came across one unusual association in the unlikely surroundings of a former naval barracks. In the post=war years the "von Holst" Department of the Max Planck Institute was temporarily housed at Wilhelmshaven. The ground floor was put at the scientists' disposal and space was at a premium. One of the former messrooms was turned into a laboratory and a mezzanine floor was added, making a kind of "loft" with access only by ladder. Frau von Keiser, technical assistant at the Institute, was determined not to be separated from the pugs which she had brought through the war with considerable difficulty. She had the bright idea of keeping her pugs in the "loft" above the laboratory where she worked all day. They could not get down the ladder and she was able to keep an eye on them without interfering with her duties. The laboratory was full of vivaria and glass tanks containing praying mantises, stick insects and chameleons — and she was kept fully occupied.

I paid a special visit to Wilhelmshaven, not to see the pugs but to photograph the bird orientation experiments of Dr Gustav Kramer, who was later to meet a tragic fate, falling from a cliff face when looking at a rock dove's nest. The pugs were merely incidental, but from a comparatively trivial beginning our acquaint=ance grew over the years and developed into a story in its own right.

My first introduction to Mombo, the ancestor of numerous generations of pugs, was in the "loft" above the tanks of insects. Many of the pug puppies which I saw on that occasion have since become grandparents and great=grandparents and their progeny continue to increase. Frau von Keiser, known by everyone as "Keiserin", now has her own pug house at Seewiesen which was specially built to meet her requirements. When I went to see her last spring there were so many pugs that it was difficult to find anywhere to put a foot down without treading on them. Eighteen pure=bred pugs of British, Dutch and German descent all tried to greet me at the same time. The room was divided into two with a wooden barrier to enable the "Keiserin" to work at her desk in peace. There were five small sleep= ing boxes in the other half of the room and in these pugs of all ages lolled on cushions. In a slightly raised position, overlooking the general hurly=burly, lay my old friend Mombo from Wilhelmshaven. His face had become grey and the folds more pronounced with the passing of the years. He was in wonderful con= dition and was still the acknowledged boss.

For many years Mombo had had a co=ruler in the shape of a huge cock known as Koko. Mombo shared his authority over the pugs quite voluntarily with Koko. The cock had grown up with the pugs from a chick. He had become so attached to them — he was so imprinted on them — that over the years he had grown up beside Mombo playing a kind of instructor's role. A good cock maintains strict discipline in his hen=house. Koko dealt with the pugs in the manner of his species and gained their respect, often by force. In ordinary life the cock is not only the despot but also the "watch=dog" and Koko assumed this role with the pugs. He always accompanied the dogs on walks in the forest. When some of the more lively pugs indulged in boisterous squabbles, the cock immediately took up a posi= tion between the two contestants and apparently took them to task. This happened on several occasions when I was present. It was astonishing to see the prompt reaction of the dogs. If the cock scolded them they took up submissive positions by walking in front of him. On occasions, after a scene of this nature, it looked to me as though the cock took one of the pugs on one side and said to it: "You just come along with me."

Koko looked after his "flock" with great thoroughness. He protected his pugs from all strangers and from anything which appeared to him, for some reason or other, to be hostile. All this was of great interest to the behaviour observers but unfortunately Koko's attacks became fiercer with age. He had no respect for children if they happened to come too close; he would knock the smaller ones over and then trample on them, injuring them with his sharp spurs. He would not even give way before adults.

In the interests of general safety Koko had to be parted from Mombo and his pugs. The giant cock was given command over some members of his own kind. Some good resulted from the removal of Koko. Certain experiments which Koko would never have tolerated could then be undertaken with the pugs.

CHAPTER 32

One of Nature's Mysteries

THEY LOOKED SO alike that they might have been twins. They had the same rounded form of head, their features looking very similar over the little muzzle; their legs and bodies were of the same size and they were both blind. They were puppies but they were not born in the same litter. In fact, they came from widely different breeds: one was a mastiff, the other a dachshund; but at this early age they resembled each other closely. Anneliese Maier, who breeds mastiffs at the Hermitage kennels in Munich, laughingly held up the puppies side by side for me to see. "Which is the mastiff?" she asked. "This one? Or is that the dachs= hund?" I could not tell them apart.

Bambi, the dachshund, was ten days old and Lucius, the mastiff, was only three days old. They were both eight and a half inches long, measured from the head along the back. They retained their twin=like appearance for a short time only. When I went to see them eleven days later I could not possibly have confused them. Lucius already exceeded Bambi by two and a quarter inches even though the dachshund was a week older. Bambi's face was already lengthening noticeably, whereas Lucius' head was showing more massive proportions.

At my next visit Anneliese held the two puppies up so that their heads were on the same level, with the result that Bambi's legs dangled in the air whereas Lucius stood firmly on the table. At this stage both puppies were showing the typical characteristics of their breeds and in the weeks that followed they started to explore their surroundings.

By the time that Bambi was three months old, he came precisely up to the ankles of his mastiff friend. At six months the dachshund had almost grown to his final size and he was already mentally mature. This was obvious from his conduct and behaviour when compared with Lucius; dachshunds mature early. The big mastiff still had another four months to go before attaining full size and, according to the breeder, it would be another twelve months before Lucius would have caught up with Bambi mentally.

The mastiff and the dachshund are members of the same species and yet one is a "giant" and the other a "dwarf". They start life resembling each other so closely that we cannot tell them apart, but as they grow the remarkable differences between these two breeds become apparent. One of the mysteries of nature? The embryo holds the secret.

CHAPTER 33

Four Dachshunds Are Born

BIRTHS TAKE PLACE every day and yet the wonders of creation are such that it never seems to be an everyday matter. I wanted to photograph the birth of some dachshund puppies and a pedigree bitch named Schnitzi was expecting a litter at the Hermitage Kennels in Munich. I arrived on time but Schnitzi gave no indication of producing her litter, and for some days we took it in turns to watch her and to take her for walks in the garden. We knew from experience that it was a good thing to keep the mother moving and one night it looked as though labour might be starting. There was a hurried telephone call to the vet as we feared that Schnitzi would not manage without assistance. Although it was night= time the vet agreed to come. In the meantime we massaged her, trying to assist her weak efforts. She seemed to know that we were trying to help and licked our hands.

The puppies appeared to be in no hurry to face the world and the vet gave Schnitzi a pain=killing injection. From time to time she panted heavily but the hours went by and still nothing happened. The room was silent except for the ticking of the clock. It was at five minutes to five in the morning that the alarm clock suddenly went off (someone had wound it up by mistake) and Schnitzi gave a tremendous heave and the miracle happened: a pale shiny sac lay alongside her. Now and again something moved inside the elongated object; the newly born creature was trying to burst out of its transparent cage, which looked like a cellophane wrapping. A thin white string — the navel cord — still connected it to the mother. Schnitzi was too weak to open the transparent sac with her teeth and so the vet assisted. The flashlight went off and I had a record of the puppy at the moment of birth.

Schnitzi then bit through the navel cord and the tiny creature lay there, quite free and fully formed, a complete little dog. But it made no sound. We then held it carefully by the hind legs so that its head hung down and gently tapped it on the nape of the neck until it gave a faint but audible squeak. Life began: the lungs inhaled and the small black body expanded. Schnitzi then dried the puppy with her rough tongue, nudging it up and down with her nose; it gave a few squeaks as she pulled it in all directions, drying it all over. This massaging stimulated the circulation of the blood.

This first puppy in the litter was named Bella. She soon gained strength and only a few minutes after her birth she was already tottering along on her front legs, crawling towards her mother. Bella was thirsty, and, with what seemed to us miraculous instinct, she found the nipple after a few false starts. As she drank the life=giving liquid she smacked her lips. Her enjoyment, however, was short=lived. Schnitzi shook her off abruptly and a fawn=coloured puppy now lay beside Bella. This one was a little boy and Bella's brother was named Burschi.

All the puppies in this litter were given names beginning with B. The puppies in Schnitzi's first litter all had names beginning with A. Schnitzi herself was born in her mother's third litter and she was registered in the pedigree stud book as Claudia of Roggenstein.

Some hours later Schnitzi produced two more puppies, Butzi and Bianca. The difficulty of these births indicated that Schnitzi was already somewhat overbred. Mongrels and robust bitches rarely need the assistance of a vet. The mastiffs at the Hermitage Kennels, for instance, often take their mistress by surprise and she finds a whole litter without the bitch having given any previous indication.

I visited the four little Bs every week. Schnitzi regarded me as one of the family and allowed me to stroke her puppies without growling at me. As each day went by they became plumper, more lively and more cheeky. Their eyes were open after twelve days. For a time they appeared to be looking through a blue opaque film but this cleared gradually and their individual personalities began to develop. Burschi, the only male in the litter, was always a little fractious; he seemed more stupid than his sisters and often whined with no apparent cause. The three girls, however, were extremely lively and while Burschi sat in the basket with his head on his paws, his sisters would romp about, squealing like teenagers. The time would soon come for them to leave their mother and join a human family. And they would doubtless rule the whole household with the droll tyranny which is typical of dachshunds.

Acknowledgements

The photographs and observations in this book were made with the generous help of the following institutions:
Augsburg Zoo
Bremerhaven Animal Grotto
Duke of Croy's Estate, Dülmen, Westphalia
Arab Stud at Achental, Grassau, Upper Bavaria
Heidelberg Zoo
Dr Georg von Opel's Reserve for Animal Research, Kronberg/Taunus
Hellabrunn Zoo, Munich
Swiss National Circus (Knie Brothers)
Wilhelma Zoo, Stuttgart
Zurich Zoo
Max Planck Institute for Behaviour Physiology, Seewiesen.

*

The author wishes to thank the following in particular for their invaluable advice:
Professor Heini Hediger (Zurich)
Professor Erich von Holst (Seewiesen, deceased)
Professor Konrad Lorenz (Seewiesen)
Dr Georg von Opel (Kronberg)
as well as all the animal keepers who, by their untiring co=operation, made it possible for him to take photographs and make observations.